Hereward College

LEARNING RESOURCES
CENTRE

A year in the life of Frankie Dettori

To my mother
Iris Maria Niemen
All my love
Frankie

A year in the life of
Frankie
Dettori

FRANKIE DETTORI

HEINEMANN : LONDON

First published in Great Britain 1996
by William Heinemann
an imprint of Reed International Books Ltd
Michelin House, 81 Fulham Road, London SW3 6RB
and Auckland, Melbourne, Singapore and Toronto

A CIP catalogue record for this title
is available from the British Library

ISBN 0 434 00365 4

Typeset by Falcon Oast Graphic Art
in 12 on 15 point Plantin
Printed and bound in Great Britain by
Clays Ltd, St. Ives PLC

Contents

Preface   vii

1   The Young Lanfranco   1

2   My Apprenticeship   17

3   Overcoming a Crisis   33

4   Champion Jockey   51

5   A Typical Season   69

6   The Start of the 1996 Season   93

7   The 2,000 Guineas   113

8   Injury   127

9   Road to Recovery   141

10   The Comeback   151

11   The Race of the Year   163

12   Super Saturday   179

13   The St Leger   191

Acknowledgements

My fiancée Catherine Allen
Tony Stafford
Matty Cowing
John Gosden and Rachel Hood
Peter Burrell and Christopher Little
The Maktoum family
Clare Bancroft
Colin and Andy
Gianfranco Dettori
Alessandra Dettori

Preface

Just when I thought I'd finished writing this book, something like that had to happen. I thought I could relax for a while and wind down, but then along came Ascot. It's hard to win the National Lottery, but there is one winner at least nearly every week. My seven out of seven, in all seven races, on the first day of the Festival of British Racing on 28 September 1996 was truly a first.

It seems that never in England, or anywhere else in the world, had a jockey gone through the card in a seven-race programme until my wonderful, brilliant, unbelievable day. And what a day to choose: national television coverage, a big crowd, great racing and the support on the day of most of the people who have helped me so much throughout the years, and whose story you will read in the following pages.

We travelled up to Ascot with a single race on our minds. Mark Of Esteem had given me two of my greatest moments during the topsy-turvy year in which injury and suspension, funnily enough not just for me but for so many of my friends and colleagues in the weighing room, had been as much a factor as big race wins. Walter Swinburn, who was the jockey closest to beating me on one of those Saturday seven stars, had been almost killed in a fall in Hong Kong at the start of the year. Willie Carson, who had won six races out of seven one day at Newcastle in 1990, was still in hospital after his awful accident when he'd been kicked and close to dying in the same Newbury parade ring where I'd broken my elbow back in June and lost any chance of retaining my title. But, as we hoped that Willie's health would get better just as Walter's had, I was reflecting that seven out seven would be better, in the context of my career, than seventy-seven championships. Although don't think I'm going to be satisfied with the two I've had so far.

In the days since that memorable occasion at Ascot, when racing went onto the front pages for the first time for all the right reasons, I have never stopped thinking about the enthusiasm, warmth, kindness and sheer excitement that the 20,000 people at Ascot showed that afternoon. Each win got a better response than the one before. The other jockeys started by being frustrated as I kept on winning, but even Pat Eddery, who I had to beat three times, Mick Kinane, Walter Swinburn, Ray Cochrane and the others actually began to share and enjoy (almost) the atmosphere. They would all rather have won a race, but their chance came on the Sunday.

It might look as though it was my day. But for me it was horse racing's day. The people's day. An occasion to show that a day at the races can be as much fun as any football match, tennis final or golf tournament. We have a great sport in our hands. It's up to us, the people who are identified by the public as the leading players, to fuel that enthusiasm. I loved the responsibility of all the interviews. It's always at the back of your mind that media attention can be cruel, but for once all the exposure was positive and I loved it.

But to come back to Mark Of Esteem. The way he won the Queen Elizabeth II Stakes, Europe's mile championship, against six other top-class horses, gave me the most astonishing feeling I've ever had for a single performance. When we turned for home up the final straight at Ascot, all had been going well, but I knew that in Bosra Sham, the 1,000 Guineas winner, we had a top performer to catch. Pat sent her on by the two-furlong pole but with my horse still going so easily I decided to wait – as I hadn't when he'd won the 2,000 Guineas, when I'd asked him about 100 yards too soon. This time I delayed his challenge until the furlong pole, and the way Mark Of Esteem quickened showed the difference between a great horse like Bosra Sham and a true champion. It was exhilarating and such a joy to come back and meet Sheikh Maktoum and Sheikh Mohammed, whose family's support for me has been so constant and such a great part of my career.

That was the third winner in the royal-blue colours of Godolphin, following the first two races, the Cumberland Lodge Stakes with Wall Street and the Diadem Stakes with Diffident. The Diadem Stakes was probably the one race where I needed a slice of luck. We beat Lucayan Prince by a short head. Walter had not been able to get out for a clear run until it was too late. If he had and had beaten us, I could have spent the rest of my life moaning that David Loder, another of the trainers who has been a great influence on me over the past years, ruined my moment of history.

After the big race and Mark Of Esteem, it was wonderful that John Gosden should get in on the act. John is much more than my boss. He's a friend, a great man and really my mentor. His horse Decorated Hero had top weight in the Tote Festival Handicap. He won so easily. He'd have got there – and from a bad draw in twenty-two out of twenty-six – if he'd carried 10st 13lbs, never mind the actual 9st 13lbs.

And so it went on, Fatefully giving us a fourth Godolphin win in the fillies' handicap and then Lochangel, half-sister to my lovely old friend Lochsong, making all – despite the trainer Ian Balding's instructions to hold her up and give her a chance – to win the Blue Seal Stakes in great style.

So now it was a big field, another top weight and a full two miles of the testing Ascot circuit for Fujiyama Crest, trained by one of the greatest trainers, Michael Stoute. The reception on the way to the start was sensational and, having realised in the morning I would be on a 12–1 chance in that last race, it was a shock to see in the paddock as I waited to get on the horse that he was 2–1 favourite. But, as they say, Fujiyama Crest didn't know he was a 2–1 shot, not until the canter to the start anyway.

As we went past the post on the first circuit, I took the lead and, all the way round, the horse was moving nicely within himself. All the time I was waiting for them to come and swallow me up, but when we got to the straight I was still ahead. Later, Ray Cochrane asked me, 'Did you hear the crowd as we turned for home?' and, thinking about it, he was right. It was incredible. The noise began there and, as we thrust for the line, got louder and louder. I could sense Pat Eddery and Northern Fleet coming up. The crowd knew what they wanted. I'm sure Fujiyama Crest knew, too. He must have read the script the night before as he stood in his stable at Newmarket. Pat and Northern Fleet kept coming, but the crowd and Fujiyama Crest just wouldn't let him go by.

I was there! It was an amazing feeling. The usual cliché from a sportsman is that 'it didn't sink in until …' I'm sure in this case it will never sink in. Certainly, until my first loser the next day it was possible to imagine it never ending. But, as the wonderful people who stood and cheered for so long on the Saturday night discovered, it's like the lottery. It's a once in a lifetime achievement. Unlike the lottery, my seven out of seven was a once in everyone's lifetime achievement.

1 The Young Lanfranco

Well, here I am, twenty-five years old, twice champion jockey in England and it's all flown past me like a fast-running river. Who would have believed that the little Italian boy in Milan would find himself living in England – for the past ten years – and writing a book about some of his experiences in those times?

Writing a book indeed. In my school days I read only one book, *Twenty Thousand Leagues Under The Sea*, by Jules Verne, and now I'm writing one myself, and in English! That wasn't because I was dumb at school. No, I was one of those middle-of-the-road people. I was actually pretty smart, picking things up first time. But all the time I was trying to get away with doing as little as possible, not wanting to be too much of a swot. I found mathematics very easy, thought geography was very interesting, but didn't enjoy the other subjects much.

Apart from that there was football. Always football. We

went to school from eight thirty in the morning until five o'clock. We had our lunch break between twelve-noon and two and were supposed to take between twelve and twelve thirty to eat and digest the food. But of course we gobbled it up as fast as we could and by about five minutes after twelve we were picking the sides for football.

We were always about twenty a side and played for an hour and a half every afternoon in the hot Italian sun. We would rip our jeans and need a new pair of shoes every week, but I must say it was the best time of my life. I was always the one standing on the goal-line, the goal-hanger, waiting for the ball to come to touch it past the goalkeeper. If I didn't score fifteen goals in an afternoon I would be disappointed.

Apart from the size of the teams and the fact there was no offside, our game was different from real football in a more significant way. It's funny that the school only had basket-balls because the main sport there was basketball in the hall. So we used a basketball for our games. It was so heavy for a kid – it was like kicking a pot plant around the place.

The football helped take away some of the unhappiness that I always felt at home. My father was a jockey, a very successful one, but there was never much contact between us. Being a jockey is a pressure job, and when things don't go well, you take your losers home. He would always put the paper up, studying the racecard for the next day.

My father was always cold. I remember when I was about six years old, me and my sister, who is six years older than me, might want to play and he would be in a bad mood. We lived in a kind of villa and we could not go out to play in the garden because he would be resting there, preparing for riding the next day. We would kiss him goodnight and go to our room early.

When I was six I was forced to ride a pony for the first time. Me and my friends, whose fathers were also jockeys, used to enjoy going to the races, but only really to play football with the other kids. Funnily enough, most of those boys are also jockeys now. At that time nothing was further from my mind than being a jockey, but it all changed when my sister ran away from home.

My parents had divorced when I was six months old. I stayed with my mum until I was five but then, when it was time to go to school, she suggested: 'Stay with Dad, he's got more money than us.' He did not live far away, so that's what happened.

Life was very strict with my father and stepmother. But without that experience I would never have been able to come to England aged fourteen. My stepmother's toughness on us when we were young made that possible.

I suppose for me there was a lack of love. In those days I was very much into myself and my true character did not really come out until later. It was worse still for my sister, Sandra, though. She had a rejection feeling about our stepmother. There would be tears every night, particularly when my sister knew she was in the wrong. She would fight anyway, just wanting to prove a point. For me, I was quite a little boy, learning all about these things, so I thought, Why fight? Still do what you want but not get caught, not get found out. In other words, I developed a little native cunning.

This went on for a couple of years. All the time we had our duties. I would have to prepare the table for dinner, my sister would clear up after. At eight thirty I would have to go to bed; she was allowed to stay up until nine o'clock, but by eight thirty she would already be in an argument so she would go to bed when I did. Then we would cry together, but while she could not wait to get away, I would still have my toy car to play with, so I was less unhappy than her.

Then, when she was fourteen, she ran away from Dad and went back to Mum. Dad asked her to come back but she didn't want to. Then something happened that would end up changing my life. In all the time we'd been with Dad, he'd never taken me to school. But the day after my sister went away he dropped me at school, for the first and last time! Otherwise, I walked there every day. Soon after, I came out of school and he had come to pick me up – in a horsebox. 'Hey Dad,' I said. 'Jump in,' he said. I jumped in and he was carrying on as usual about how bad my sister was.

Anyway, he took me to a horse farm, owned by one of the Italian owners with horses running at the San Siro track in Milan. I'll never forget it. It seems like yesterday. He said hello to the owner who showed us three ponies in a field. He pointed to the ponies and said: 'Which do you like?' At my age it was like taking an adult to the Ferrari shop and asking, 'Which car you would like?'

There were two bay ponies and one palomino, with four white socks, white tail, mane and face. Of course I took the palomino. We put her in the horsebox and took her home. We stabled her at a local farm, which in those days still kept cows and made their own milk, but it is no longer there. Dad taught me how to muck out, put the bedding on the floor. He gave me a bag with tools and taught me how to clean her and how to use the hoof-pick. He said: 'This is it, your toy. You will look after her. After school, you will come to muck out, feed and ride her.'

Every day, I could not wait to finish school. I'd run home to put on my jodhpurs and my jockey silks in the famous colours of Carlo d'Allessio, and run to the pony, who was about a quarter of a mile away from home.

I would not be able to wait to ride her, so instead of mucking out first, I'd hide the droppings in the corner. I'd sling the saddle on and go straight out and gallop for the hell of it. It was a big circuit all round the outside of the farm. The pony was called Sylvia and soon I would tell all my classmates to come and watch me and Sylvia. Near the farm there was a kind of showjumping ring, very run down and falling to bits. As I rode past the little grandstand there, all my mates would shout: 'Vae Lanfranco!'

From then I always wanted to be a jockey. About a year after my sister left home, when I was nine, all the local ponies were entitled to run in the Pony Derby, staged on the racecourse at San Siro during June. I became a man with a mission. I would get Sylvia ready each day and gallop her in preparation for the Derby. When we got to the race, though, all the ponies were giants compared to Sylvia, all the riders were giants compared to me. My only advantage was that my pony would carry much less weight than the others.

It did help that for years I had been to the track twice a week to watch my dad. The course was made on the jumping track between the last two fences, probably around three furlongs. As we waited for the start, though, I was a nervous wreck and when the flag was dropped I missed the kick and crossed the finish stone last. Sylvia then saw the finishing flag, dug in her toes and I fell over her head and straight into the water jump! I got out dripping wet and jumped back on. My first experience of race riding was hardly an unqualified success!

After about a year the novelty was gone. Of course I loved my pony, but every day after I finished school I was supposed to muck her out and exercise her. By the time the winter came, it was really cold. I suppose I got lazy and if she wasn't exercised one day she would be twice as fresh the next. Once, I left her four days in the box after she'd dropped me but there was no one there to advise me. She definitely had got the better of me. By this time I'd got scared and never had control of her.

Luckily, Dad saw the signs and finally sold the pony, and I went right off racing for a year. But then, just as suddenly, aged around eleven, I became interested again. I began to bet on the races – but I could hardly reach up to the window to place my bets. That was the age when we all began to think we were the business. We would wear trendy jeans but still we'd play football, now with a small ball, between the races. Sometimes we would take branches from the trees and pretend to run our own races, whacking our own legs in time as if hitting a horse to make it go faster.

Then we'd hear the commentator say that the horses were going into the stalls, and run across to the window to place our bets. Usually it would be the minimum stake on a short-priced favourite, say a 2–1 on chance, and we'd be delighted to get our money back. This was when I really got the love of horse-racing. I would go with Dad when he would look round the yards with the trainers. That was when I finally knew I just had to be a jockey.

By the time I was twelve, during the school holidays, it was arranged that I would ride in the d'Allessio stable. For three months I walked and trotted round the roads, and then had to get down for someone else to do a canter. You could hardly say I was learning much.

In those days, starting early was not unusual, unlike now when sixteen is the minimum age. But I began at thirteen and was one of the last to do so. Then it was really a case of: 'You know how to count to ten; how to sign cheques; it's off to the real world!'

Dad sat me down. 'So you want to be a jockey?' To my stepmother, I was just a quiet little boy with no motivation. But really she never gave me a chance to show what I could do. She was too aggressive. When she and my Dad were around I was too scared to be outgoing. They thought there was not enough aggression in me to become a jockey. But at school I was the naughtiest boy in the class!

Dad and me had our first 'man talk'. He told me, 'You might want to become a jockey but it's not easy. For most boys who come into stables, nearly all of them only get to look after their three horses, only one in a thousand makes it as a jockey.'

Despite Dad's pessimism, I started soon after with the d'Allessio stable. Dad had been first jockey there for fifteen years and won nearly everything in Italian racing when Luca Cumani's father, Sergio, was the trainer. I remember going there sometimes on Tuesday mornings, the main work day, before school, when I was about seven or eight years old. Bolkonski, who later came to England to win the 2,000 Guineas, was one of Dad's regular rides for Mr Cumani, as was Wollow.

The first racehorse I ever sat on was an old sprinter called Or Bettelo. I was seven or eight years old and he was about ten. After he'd done his work I would walk him around. He knew so much about racing I'm sure he could read and write! In truth, he walked me around! One day, Mr Cumani gave me some lumps of sugar to give to the horse and then put me on top. Looking down, I could not believe how far the ground was.

By the time I came into racing, Mr Cumani, sadly, had died from cancer, and Mr Botti had taken over. The stable was still the classiest in Italy, a bit like Vincent O'Brien at his peak, with forty horses all Group or Listed class. When

Mr d'Allessio died, the empire collapsed.

With Mr Botti, I was given the same horse to exercise first and second lots, as he took so much work. My first four or five months I didn't learn anything. Dad was too busy, except on Tuesdays for one and a half hours when he would shout and scream at me the whole time: 'Pull your jerks up; put your bum down; lean a bit more forward; do the arch this way.' I'd make a big point to do as he told me but by second lot I'd immediately go back to riding 'cowboy style'. That was my John Wayne impression: left hand holding on to the neck strap, choking the horse; right hand up near the chest; legs out straight in front, like Eddie 'the Eagle' Edwards doing a ski-jump.

I wasn't learning much, but for the first time I had a feeling of being myself. It was like when I was a kid and was able to go out on my bike, that sort of freedom. I felt like a man, as though I was achieving something. At first, when I was working in the stables, I was very slow. It took me half an hour to groom each horse, but at the end of that time, the horse would be really spotless. I loved the work.

One guy I remember especially from that time is Raffaeli Lai. He taught me a few things about horses; how to do them up, generally everything about grooming. He was horse mad and still is. The funny thing was that ten years later I ended up riding his horse, Misil, for him and we finished second in the Coral-Eclipse at Sandown and also ran well in the Prix de l'Arc de Triomphe at Longchamp. Happily for Raffaeli, we won the Gran Premio del Jockey Club at San Siro at the end of 1993. Raffaeli is now married to an English girl, Sandra, and every summer they stay for three weeks with his in-laws and always come to New-market to see me.

Apart from Raffaeli, my time in the Botti stable was pretty

unrewarding. For those few months all I had to show was riding the same horse every day. He was so fat, so lazy, I had to push him all the time. We were always at the back of the string when he went out to exercise, never at the front.

Then, when that season was ending in Milan and Rome, Dad was already miles ahead, probably by eighty winners, in the jockeys' title race and already champion. At that stage of the year he would always take a little holiday and then ride abroad in jockeys' championship events around the world. In the season, therefore, I hardly ever saw him because he was busy racing; in the winter he was always away. To me, most of the time, Dad was little more than a ghost.

This autumn, he sat down with my stepmother to decide what I should do. Winters in Milan can be very cold with plenty of snow and the horses training there do nothing. Dad had a good friend from his own wild teenage years called Antonio Verdicchio. Dad knew him as Tonino. He had a stable in Pisa, where the winters are much milder, and Dad called and asked him whether he would take me into the stable to live and work with him. Tonino said he would be delighted to do so, and off I went to Pisa.

Tonino had three daughters, and the move there gave me the first chance to find the real me. This trainer took me on like his own son – the son he'd never had himself, I suppose. Dad had told him, 'Make him work hard, pay him peanuts each month and be sure he does his three.' Antonio kept to the first two parts of Dad's request anyway.

He met me at the station in a big white Mercedes and took me back to change into my jodhpurs – he wore a jacket and trousers – and then we went down to the stables, an L-shaped building containing twenty-five horses. I said to him: 'Tonino, Dad told me you would be giving me my three horses to do.' He tutted and shook his head. He said: 'You start at one end and I'll start at the other. We'll meet in the middle.' We each had a barrow and a fork. That was evening stables à la Tonino!

I found it a bit difficult. By the time I did the first three, he'd done ten. He came to inspect my efforts. 'Don't throw all that straw away,' he said, throwing it back into the boxes. For the little boy used to living at the other end of the scale in racing stables, this was a real culture shock. I was being thrown into the real world where most people are strugglers.

Then the head lad arrived, late and unshaven. He was called Chipola, and by the time he arrived there were only two horses to muck out. He opened the tack room. There was no such thing as a work list for the horses' programme for the following day and the tack would be slung on to anything in the room.

The work riding was done by Tonino, me and Chipola, who must have weighed nearly seventeen stone. The first morning we put the tack on three horses and took them out to the exercise track, which was about six furlongs round and on sand. I was to do a canter on a ten-year-old gelding called Grunland. We went on to the track and started to canter. That was fine, but at the end of the circuit I tried to stop him and couldn't. After the fourth lap I started to scream 'Help!' Tonino shouted out, 'Stop screaming and pull.' He wasn't going very fast by that time, but however hard I pulled he didn't respond. He had a 'wooden' mouth and he eventually only stopped when Tonino got off his horse, held on to him with one hand and stood in the middle of the track with his arms wide open. As soon as he saw Tonino, the old thief stopped in a stride.

I thought to myself: 'I really messed that up. If that had happened in Milan I would have been fired on the spot.' So

I stood there waiting for Tonino to give me a bollocking. All he said was. 'Look, stop screaming. Save your breath and pull!' We rode either seven or eight lots every day, going in and out, slinging the tack on and off. Suddenly, after only riding one horse in Milan, I would be on eight different horses every day. Inevitably, I'd fall off at least once each morning, and we'd work through till about one o'clock. I'd be absolutely knackered, so usually, after lunch, I'd sleep until six, go back for evening stables, then wait for the girls to come back from school.

We'd go out playing in the street with some of the other local kids. On Sundays there was a disco locally for the teenagers and we'd always go there. I was my own man. No one told me when to come home, when to go to bed. Life was beautiful. As for the riding, within a month I was riding shorter than Lester Piggott, confident as anyone on a horse. I knew all the horses and once a week Marco Paganini, one of the top jockeys, who was later to be killed in a riding accident, came to ride work. From being wrapped in cotton wool, here I was finding freedom and my own personality. Tonino gave me everything, never screamed or shouted, and the nice thing was we helped him train a few winners in the months I was there.

When Dad picked me up in Pisa at the end of April, by which time I was fourteen, I had enjoyed the best four months of my career at that stage. I would ride anything, and was fearless, never minding falling off. Of course, when I came back home, I went straight back into my shell, but Dad could not believe his own eyes how much I had improved. As soon as I got back, I was riding fast work with the top jockeys. Final gallops before the races, and I rode short. They put me on hard pullers, anything. In the d'Allessio stable I even led my dad in work at fourteen, and

I was one of the best riding lads in the stable. Once on a horse I felt good and Dad soon saw something in me; saw I could make it one day, so he started planning for my future.

Within a month the brainwashing began. I'm sure he'd already had the plan in his mind, but didn't tell me, I guess. He thought I was young and would not be race-riding for another year, so arranged for me to spend six months with Luca Cumani in England, then six months with Patrick Biancone in Chantilly and be back in Italy at fifteen and a half ready to become a jockey.

He explained it all to me and I said I didn't want to go. We went to the races that day, me in between Dad and my stepmother. He said: 'Lester Piggott and Pat Eddery have aeroplanes, take rides in helicopters and get to ride the best horses in the top races.' By the time we got to the track, between the pair of them they'd managed to brainwash me and soon I was to be off.

The stay in England was meant to be six months, and Dad gave me £366, almost a million lire, all in those big £20 notes. Imagine the young Lanfranco, unable to speak a word of English, due to spend six months in a foreign country. I was meant to leave in the spring, but just before my departure date, I was out riding my moped, slipped on some wet turf and shattered my elbow. I needed two operations and the scar is still visible.

I did not finally leave until early July, dressed like a nice English boy with a suit and tie and carrying a big suitcase. When I got to Luton airport, a taxi driver, holding a sign with 'Lanfranco Dettori' written in large letters, met me and we set off for Newmarket. The journey took about an hour and he turned on the radio, and we heard what I realised was a race commentary. It was the Princess of Wales's Stakes and Petoski won it.

The driver took me to my digs in Bury Road, in Newmarket, but I guess everyone was out at the races. We left my suitcase outside the door, at the driver's suggestion. I was amazed. In Italy if you leave anything like that they'll take it. But the driver said: 'No problem.' He took me down to the stables, and left me in Luca Cumani's office.

In Italy in those days, most trainers' offices would comprise a table, a lamp, the entries, some pens and a telephone. Here, there were computers, two secretaries, trophies and pictures on the wall of all Mr Cumani's big winners. As for the stable itself, my reaction was, 'Wow!' All the doors were in the right place, polished, and there were no dogs, sheep or cats to make things untidy.

So my first memory of England was getting to the office from where the secretary guided me to the stable and introduced me to the head lad (Old Arthur). He grabbed me by the arm, opened a box and slid it open. I didn't understand at first what he wanted, until he put a dandy brush in my hand. I hung my jacket up on the door, and dressed the horse over. At five o'clock, Luca Cumani came. Everyone seemed so frightened of him. It was as though Hitler's come! Everyone panicked, running everywhere like wildcats. I was pretty nervous too, as I'd only met this guy for a few minutes once in Pisa. He had those smouldering eyes which looked at you. Who would have believed that I would stay with him for seven years?

Luca had an Italian assistant, Stefano Ibido. He didn't talk to me much – he didn't want to be a babysitter, I suppose. Each night, the guv'nor would come at five o'clock. You'd stand by, take off the chain and feed the horse. He came into my stall, and you could hear a pin drop; it was like being in a church. He just said: 'Bienvenuto. We pull out at six o'clock,' and moved away. I thought: 'This is gonna be a long six months.' But by the end of that season, I guess they must have liked me – and I became confident enough so that within three months I'd become really cheeky.

I stayed in a bed and breakfast in Bury Road. They really tried hard to make me feel at home. Soon after I got there they served me up a meal with Heinz ravioli, obviously trying to give me a taste of home. It was really kind of them to try that, but I only managed to eat the stuff out of respect for them, not for the food itself. My room was the smallest in the house, only a bed and sink really. The one 'luxury' was a bottle of orange squash which was left for me. I'd never seen it in Italy and didn't realise you had to dilute it with water.

Life then was just work and bed. I earned between £12 and £17 a week and the stable paid for my digs. It got to be like a prison, and the lady whose house it was had two daughters, who took the mickey out of me all the time. Then, suddenly, after three months, when I got my confidence, I started to go out at night. Colin (my best mate) and Andy, who is now my driver, were my first real friends in England and like me were apprentices with Mr Cumani. I was lucky to meet them when I did.

Those early days at Luca's gave me my first experience of the real world as lived by the young stable staff in Newmarket. When I first arrived there I was only fourteen and from the start I felt the eyes of everyone on me. I suppose they saw I was wearing all the flashy gear, and to them I was a rich kid, and my father was a champion jockey. I was always getting hit – not hard – by a lot of the older lads, but I came to see it was a bit of a joke, and not the bullying I feared at the beginning. Then, on Saturday nights, when we all used to go out, I was like the little brother and then they all made sure I was okay and looked after me. There was the usual rivalry between the lads from the different yards and at the end of a Saturday night when a few had had a little too much to drink, it was a big help that there was always someone and usually a few people there to make sure you got home safe.

It was really my first experience of going out regularly, the first time I'd been out for a drink late at night. The regular venue was the Golden Lion in Newmarket High Street. In those days, one of Luca's assistants was an Italian and he gave me some advice: 'If you go out on Saturday night, don't go to the Golden Lion.' After that, where else did I end up but at the Golden Lion? It cost £1 to get in, and the fact I was so young mattered less in Newmarket where everyone is the same size, except the trainers of course! I did look very young, though, especially in the face, but I borrowed a leather jacket which made it appear that I had shoulders like Mike Tyson. Then I would rub the print from a newspaper on top of my lip to make it look (hopefully) that I might just be eighteen. I would go and queue up with the rest of the lads from the yard and, when I got to the door, I tried to put on a deep voice to say, in my best broken English, 'How much is it please?' Then I'd pay the pound and when my age was asked, the other lads would assure them I was eighteen and stick up for me if anyone queried it.

In the event, it was pretty tame. We'd play pool in the back room for most of the night and I would have a couple of vodka and oranges because you couldn't really taste the vodka. I must say I don't really like the taste of alcohol. Then, at the end of the evening, coming up to twelve thirty a.m., the DJ would line up three or four slow records, which was the signal for everyone to try to pair up with someone.

So the cues in the back room would be dropped and we'd run on to the dance floor to look for any available girls. Sometimes you ended up with someone to go home with, or more often there would be fights with people arguing over the women.

The six months flashed by and I went home for ten days in Italy, expecting to leave after that for Mr Biancone. Luca must have said something about me to my Dad, but anyway, ten days later, instead of a trip to France, I was on my way back to England. I'd found myself, and the rest is history!

2 My Apprenticeship

I still used to go back to Italy quite a lot at this stage of my career and, unlike in Britain, where you have to be sixteen to ride in a race, in Italy you can start earlier. I had my first win as a jockey in Turin in late November, a month before my sixteenth birthday. My chance for a first success in England would not come, of course, until the following season, and it was thanks to Mr Cumani that I got my first ride the next year, on a horse trained by Peter Walwyn.

Mr Walwyn had been champion trainer, handling the great champion Grundy back in the 1970s. He was well known for his forthright views. Since then he has been a campaigner for his beloved Lambourn in Berkshire, the training centre where he has been based for so long. He is affectionately known throughout the racing world as Basil Fawlty, because of a sometimes uncanny hint of the John Cleese character in the TV show *Fawlty Towers*. The first ride came because Luca had been telling people that he had

17

a promising young rider in the stable who could ride at 7st 7lb, which was then the minimum weight to be carried in races. Mr Walwyn asked Graham Green, who was then the Press Association representative who compiled the lists of jockeys for races – now it's done through Weatherbys – who would be available for an apprentice race at Kempton at the Easter bank holiday meeting in 1987. Graham suggested me and I got that ride and also ended up on another horse, trained by Reg Akehurst.

As a total unknown, too young to drive, I had to get a lift and it was Lizzy Hare, at the time Luca's secretary, who offered to give up her bank holiday to drive me to the races. Both races were on television and I was so excited as we travelled down from Newmarket. In those days, one of the top apprentices who seemed to be getting all the limelight was Dale Gibson. I didn't know anyone in the weighing room, but suddenly this guy came up to me and announced: 'I'm Dale Gibson.' To say I was surprised is an understatement. He was very tall and really skinny, and to my eyes much too big ever to be a proper jockey. I was overawed by him, but I soon found out he is not only one of the nicest and most talented riders around, but also one of the most intelligent.

You have to realise that at this time my English had not developed much beyond writing out my betting slips in Ladbrokes, but now of course I was a jockey and could not bet any more! If I could, I might have had a pound each way on the first horse, Mustakbil, who was a 33–1 shot for the apprentice race. The horse was owned by Sheikh Hamdan Al-Maktoum and I didn't realise just how privileged I was riding for him on my first mount in England. We finished second, beaten a head by a horse ridden by Dennis McKay, and when I came in I must have been a little too full of myself. Mr Walwyn probably expected a polite 'thank you' and not much more from this raw apprentice and I'm sure now that my post-race comments were not the most sensible. When he asked me how did it go, I said: 'Not fit.' 'What?' came back the answer in best Basil Fawlty style. 'Not fit.' 'Not fit?' he repeated, and by now it was almost as much a comedy as the TV series. 'Not fit, too fat,' I concluded, and with that I took the saddle off and went straight into the jockeys' room. After that exchange, it may not surprise anyone that Peter 'banned' me for a year. My other mount was favourite, but, still excited after my initial 'success', I sent him off five lengths clear in a twenty-horse race and he stopped dead as soon as we got to the home straight.

The next morning, Mr Walwyn rang Luca and said: 'That chicken of an apprentice of yours told me one of my horses was too fat. He'll not ride for me for a year.' He was as good as his word, but a year later at Folkestone he gave me another chance on a sprinter of his. He was quite well fancied, second favourite for a six-furlong maiden race. We jumped out, and three strides out of the gate he whipped round and left me on my backside. I did not get another ride for Peter Walwyn until a few years later, when I rode in the 2,000 Guineas on Sheikh Hamdan Al-Maktoum's Mukaddamah.

It was appropriate that my first winner in England should be on the filly named after Lizzy Hare, my driver to Kempton that day and a lady to whom I owed a lot for all her help while she was Luca's secretary. Colin Rate, now my closest friend and a fellow apprentice in those days, looked after her namesake and rode the filly first time out at Yarmouth, where she finished out the back. Not surprisingly, Luca didn't fancy her chances in the race at Goodwood's evening meeting and Lizzy again drove me to the track. The favourite was a horse of Sheikh Hamdan's, trained by John Dunlop, who had finished very close up in a decent race at Ascot. Lizzy was a 12–1 shot and Colin, of course, led me up. By this time I'd had about ten rides. In the race I was pushing away at the three-furlong pole, on the inside. I came through inside Pat Eddery, my idol Steve Cauthen, and Gary Bardwell and went on to win. What a thrill to beat Steve and Pat, two great champions. Two weeks later, Lizzy Hare went back to Goodwood and won a handicap and she ended up winning the Del Mar Oaks at the beautiful track near San Diego in Southern California which stages top-class racing every summer.

My early wins luckily were noticed by Lester Piggott, who had set up as a trainer after his first retirement following his astonishing riding career. His stable was very well run and the winners soon flowed. One filly of his, Versatile Rose, was a great favourite of mine, and I lost both my 5lb claim on her at Leicester and my 3lb claim at Beverley. Apprentices can claim an allowance of 7lb, then 5lb and finally 3lb when competing against senior jockeys. They lose the claim either by riding a certain number of winners, or when they turn twenty-five. Versatile Rose had a more unfortunate 'fame' later on, though, as she was the horse on which Susan Piggott suffered serious injury when riding her in a gallop during the early days when she held the family's training licence. Lester was always very supportive, and even in the spring of 1996, following his final (who knows?) retirement from the saddle, he still looked a brilliant jockey when I regularly rode work with him for David Loder on the stable's classic candidates. The day after I lost my right to claim I was due to go to Catterick again. Traffic problems cost me my first ride without a riding allowance and naturally the horse won. I did not ride another winner for almost four weeks.

To become a top jockey does not simply involve the ability to ride horses well. Of course, that is the fundamental requirement, but there are plenty of good riders out there who may not have it for one reason or another when it comes to going to the track. Seventy per cent, I feel, is the ability to ride. Then other factors come in, like the ability to communicate with trainers and owners and the temperament to handle the sort of pressures involved in a business where split-second decisions can make a large difference both in financial and prestige terms. It also helps if you can be friendly with people. The man who shows up for work with a grumpy attitude is the first to be overlooked when an opportunity arises. I'm aware of the need to communicate with people, and very few people ever react badly to a smiling face, though, of course, it helps if you mean it.

My first real break, which made my initial spurt from just another jockey to one of the people in the limelight, was soon after I finished my claim. Luca did not have a stable jockey at the time I was going through my claim, but Ray Cochrane was riding quite a bit for him. He'd won the Oaks the year before on Midway Lady for Ben Hanbury and I would say Ray had a big influence on my becoming champion apprentice and always gave me plenty of confidence. Things went well for me for the next season and then in 1989 Ray eventually became stable jockey. One day at Newmarket, where I had the mount in an apprentice race, and Ray was riding Luca's other horses, Luca was trying to sort out his plans for the next day at Haydock. He said, 'Who shall I get to ride at Haydock? Shall I get Pat (Eddery)?' Ray pointed at me and said, 'Let him ride it.' Things like that give you plenty of confidence, especially when there are a lot of potential jockeys in a yard. Ray was always helping me and pushing me forward. While Ray rode all the good horses at the big meetings in the south, I would ride lots of winners in the north and Midlands.

After I lost my claim in the summer of 1989, I had a quiet patch for a month, and then in September the winners started to flow again. Here, fate was to take a hand. Ray had already decided to accept the offer of stable jockey for Guy Harwood in 1990, and I was already champion apprentice-elect. I rode more than 100 winners, equalling the achievement of Lester Piggott, the last apprentice to achieve a century, nearly forty years before. To think we would still be riding work together forty-eight years after his first winner on the racetrack is mind-boggling! Then, Ray was one of the jockeys involved in the terrible incident in the Portland Handicap at the September meeting at Doncaster. Ray was luckier than Paul Cook and Ian Johnson, neither of whom ever rode again, but he had a broken collarbone and had to take some time off and I got to ride all the horses. I'd been getting lots of publicity in the press thanks to my winning run in the days leading up to the accident.

I was lucky enough to be given the ride on Markof-distinction, one of the stable stars, in the Kiveton Park Steel Stakes, the following day at Doncaster. Markofdistinction was a hot favourite and all the senior jockeys had their eyes on the mount, but Gerald Leigh, his owner-breeder, very kindly stuck by me. I think I rode a good race but the ground was much too soft for Markofdistinction, and he finished second to Gold Seam. Happily, I only had to wait another twenty-four hours for my first Group-race win. Races in Britain are divided into seven distinct Classes, A, B, C, D, E, F, and G. The top grade, Class A, is sub-divided into three Groups, 1, 2 and 3. Races like the Derby are Group 1, but any owner's, trainer's or jockey's ambition is to win as many Group races as possible. They are all staged on the most important tracks, almost all have national television coverage and carry plenty of prize money. My first Group-race winner was Legal Case, owned by the late Sir Gordon White, who was the main influence behind Ever Ready's sponsorship of the Epsom Derby. Sir Gordon worked closely with Lord Hanson and their Hanson Trust was the parent company of Ever Ready during the years of the sponsorship. Sir Gordon, known by everyone as Gordie, was very popular and charismatic and his death at a relatively early age a couple of years ago was very sad. The St Leger was postponed for a week that year and switched to Ayr on the following Sunday. Michelozzo and Steve Cauthen won it for Charles St George and Henry Cecil, and even if my first Classic ride on N. C. Owen finished sixth, the joy of being in that company so unexpectedly was impossible to restrain.

It seemed that I could do no wrong. Luca's stable was flying, seemingly winning races every day and, with it being common knowledge that Ray was moving next year, the better I did, the better the chance the owners would accept me as Ray's successor. One day Luca called me into the office. He told me he had spoken to my dad and to the owners and had decided he would not be employing a stable jockey. Instead it was agreed that I would ride all the horses without a retainer, but just a little money to get a car and a driver. Most of the owners were happy with the arrangement, but apparently the only question mark was the Aga Khan, for whom Ray had won the Derby in 1988 on Kahyasi. Naturally, I leapt for joy as I left the office. I'd travelled from my digs to the yard in a taxi – the little Mazda I'd bought for £200 to learn in was rusty and you had to hold the doors shut while driving. I ran home.

At the races that afternoon I did not have a particularly

good day and when I spoke to Gerald Leigh, who is one of the most successful owner-breeders in racing and the breeder of Barathea, who won the Breeders' Cup Mile for me, he said: 'I'm delighted you got the job but it may be a bit early. It could be like picking up a knife. If you grab it by the handle, you're okay: if you pick it up by the blade it can cut you and mark you for life.' Luckily for me, I started my first year – 1990 – in the Cumani job the right way. In a few days, at the two important early meetings at Newmarket and Sandown, I partnered three Group race winners: Mr Leigh's Markofdistinction in the Trusthouse Forté Mile at Sandown and Statoblest (Palace House Stakes) and Dick Hern's Roseate Tern (Jockey Club Stakes) both at Newmarket. It seems to me that I was at the right place at the right time, and took my opportunities when they came to me.

Sometimes in Britain you get the feeling that there is a little jealousy when someone does well. Luckily, in my case, the people I was working with at the Luca Cumani stable were good friends and true friends. They shared the enjoyment right from the first, when Colin Rate led up my first English winner, Lizzy Hare. As I went through my career, Colin, Andy Keates, my driver, and the rest of them were pleased for me and their reaction to me never changed in any way. Andy had a couple of rides without much luck, but he can always have that experience to help him understand what it means to be a jockey. Colin rode a little more, starting with Ben Hanbury, and had a winner or two. For apprentices in a big stable, it is hard to catch the eye of the boss and his leading people. It's hard, too, in England because school-leaving age is sixteen. By the time I was sixteen I'd had two years' experience with horses full time and was already a step ahead, without the help being my father's son obviously contributed. I suppose I was the blue-eyed boy!

Even within a stable, it gets competitive, whether it's on the gallops, where some lads I know treat every ride like the Derby, or, most important for the lads' future enjoyment, the allocation by the trainer of which young horses each lad will look after for the duration of their life in training. Usually, the main qualification is seniority and the senior lads get the best-bred, most expensive yearlings to look after. But the edge which Colin and I had was that, being light – Colin is only eight stone and I can still ride at around 8st 5lb – we were chosen to break in the new yearlings after we had been in the yard for two years. Each yearling you have to look after becomes your baby and each October you welcome your new son and/or daughter. Already, before it comes into the yard, you're dreaming, 'This is my Derby horse.' It's every stable lad's dream and obviously, in those days, it was mine.

Once the yearlings were bought to go into training with Luca, they were sent to his Fittocks stud, near Newmarket. Young racehorses are totally uneducated and the early days are the equivalent of a young person's schooling. The first step is to attach a long rope to the side of their bridle and teach them to travel in a circle. This is called lungeing and is often done in a sand ring. After they prove amenable and willing to run around in a circle, the next step is to put on a shadowroll and then the tack, trying to keep them calm and take them at whatever pace you can through this very traumatic period. We were the rodeo boys as we were light, and with yearlings, who are immature in every way, not least physically, the weight of a human body on their back can only be introduced gradually. We would lean with our stomachs on the horse's back a couple of times in the box, the horse already having been lunged by the other – heavier and stronger – lads for fifteen or twenty minutes so it was already a little tired and not fresh and ready to rear up. The next stage is to go into the ring with the horse. Again you would go and lie across his back and, still on a lunge rope, go a couple of laps like that before gradually getting your legs across him. In England this is always – in the major stables and at those studs which break in their home-breds – done in the proper way. Obviously, the time it takes to finish the process depends on the horse. Some are quick learners and the whole job is done within three or four days; in other cases, with a slow learner, it can take two to three weeks.

In Italy, in some of the places I've seen, the job is done in three days, *whatever*. The first day, you lunge them; the second, you put on the saddle and the rest of the tack; day three, you're on, rodeo style, riding them for your life. Under whichever method, by the time the process is done, the yearling is said to have been 'ridden away' and is (more or less) ready to go into the training yard with its trainer. In England, you let the horse get used to you. You have to be gentle. In those days I was much braver than I am now, and needed to be. I'm sure I could still do the job if need be and some jockeys enjoy breaking yearlings every autumn. I'm less keen on danger myself nowadays.

The trainers, busy at the yard, probably don't have either the personnel or the time themselves to ensure everything goes well, and I must confess that me and Colin were not always entirely professional in breaking yearlings. One winter in particular, at the height of the Pat Eddery–Steve Cauthen rivalry, Colin was a Pat fan, I was always Steve's follower. At Fittocks stud there was a little tack room where we would sit in front of the fire and wait for our time to go out with the horses. You would have two or three each to break every morning and after you had done that, you would then go back and continue the job with those you had broken the day before. On the last day before sending these particular yearlings to the yard, the Cauthen–Eddery rivalry spilt over into little private races with the yearlings. We took them to the paddock and pretended to be our respective heroes. Finally, we saved the two nicest ones for a big Classic race-off. Generally, we had merely trotted around the paddock, doing a Peter O'Sullevan commentary as we rode. With these two nice yearlings, both well behaved and quiet, after a couple of minutes we trotted them to the starting point, I waited for Colin to pair up and then we hacked to the telegraph poles, which acted as the finishing point. My horse had the better speed so I won that time and again the next two times. Then we had a great idea: the Gold Cup! Twice round the paddock, a total of around three furlongs, which after the earlier races was more than enough. We started the first lap at a sedate pace, going into a hack canter passing the line first time. The second time round we went at a nice swinging canter and just as we were finishing, getting close to a gallop, we were spotted by the head lad. The yearlings were blowing like mad, eyes bulging out of their heads. Everything had got a bit out of control. He had us in the tack room, and I still to this day cannot believe we never got the sack. The lucky thing for us was he didn't know this was the fourth race; he thought he caught us first time round! Fortunately, from what I remember, they both made it to the track and won races.

The reward for the lads doing the breaking in is that usually they get to make a choice from those they have been handling. I used to like to watch them when they were turned out in the paddock after being broken to see which ones looked like they wanted to run, and watch their action to see how quick they were. That year I selected a nice filly by the great stallion Danzig, whose sons and daughters were usually very good, out of a filly, Maria Weleska, who'd won the Italian Oaks. I chose her not just for her pedigree, but also because she was owned by Sheikh Mohammed, who, when he came to the stable, always gave the lads a drink. This filly took the maximum three weeks to break in. I rode her in the mornings for six months and she drove me crazy. She was a real neurotic woman and she gave me so much trouble. She drove me mad. Eventually, Mr Cumani took her off me, much to my relief. If those people in racing who are closest to the horses have no idea which is going to turn out okay, what chance have outsiders got? This filly proved that it's not always the good-looking ones that are the best, the ugly brutes can turn out better sometimes – just like people!

When I started riding, Lester Piggott had been the star rider for so many years and the generations around and just after him tried to adapt his style for themselves. Then, when Pat Eddery came to prominence, his style was the one to copy. When Steve Cauthen came to Britain, the second American age of race riding started. During the last century, Tod Sloan and his monkey-on-a-stick style was fashionable, but Steve Cauthen's success was much longer lasting. Strangely, Steve's own style was adapted for British racing; but several of the jockeys here tried to adapt his style for themselves. My father's famous words on the matter were: 'When you ride, always make an effort to look good.' I liked the look of the American style and when I saw videos of myself riding, I thought I looked neat. As it turned out, because other people thought I did look tidy, they never seemed to tell me how strong or otherwise I was in a finish. For the first couple of years riding in my style, I found it difficult, but my dad said if I kept my style, the strength would come later, and in my case it did. I'm fond of the American style. In some ways it's the same thing as riding a moped. On a moped if you want to go faster you crouch down. I suppose it's some sort of aerodynamic theory.

In the early days, if anything, I was trying too hard, crouching down from start to finish, and it's very hard physically. That's fine in America where they go flat out from the start and most of the races are shorter. Here, the pace tends to be slower and the races are longer, so I had to adapt the style. Once again it was Ray Cochrane who gave the crucial input. He would give me a kick up the bum, saying, 'Drop those jerks, you're riding too short.' That proved a really important influence and now I ride my races in two halves. Early in the race, I'm trying to relax my horses and then I'm rather higher in the saddle. Then, in the last half, when I want to go faster, I go into my American crouch. It seems to work and gives the best of both riding styles. Ray's own style is very effective and is based on strength. He is a good race-reader, but sometimes gets a little too opinionated. Like Luca though, he is a very strong character. I owe them both a lot.

For many small boys growing up, all it often takes is the suggestion 'You should try to be a jockey' and a love of animals, which many times they only find out about later, and they join the pilgrimage to one of the big stables. As I said before, even the pretty good riders, simply as riders, cannot be certain of getting more than a ride or two in a race. In ninety-five per cent of cases, the lads who start as apprentices with the ambition of making it as jockeys can only hope to be a senior stable lad. Then at least they stay in the mainstream of racing and training and still have the thrill of riding a powerful, classy thoroughbred, if only on the gallops in the morning, rather than in the Derby or the Breeders' Cup. Without the influx, it would be impossible to train all the horses which enter stables. As I explained earlier, you need the lighter lads to break in the delicate yearlings and ride the faster work with the actual jockeys. There are too many horses to 'work' – gallop fast – each day for there to be enough licensed jockeys to go round. So we tend to be selective, only getting involved in the work of the better horses or to assess a young horse for one of our trainers before its début. Ability, natural light weight, temperament, and the right attitude to work are helpful but do not guarantee success. You also need opportunity, and, if you are at the end of a line of promising boys, determination to succeed is then most important.

The snag for most who fail to make it as jockeys is that usually they have come out of studying at a time when many of their old schoolfriends may have stayed at school to gain qualifications. The experience of being outdoors in all weathers, wonderful as it can be on a nice summer morning, and tolerable at best in winter, plus the enjoyment of working with horses, often makes office work an unattractive prospect. Instead, they stay on as stable lads, work riders or as stud hands. Even though the wages in the industry are below those in many office jobs, it is a lifestyle they find hard to give up.

Throughout the racing business there are men like Gozzie, an old stableman who had a few rides in his apprentice days. He worked for Luca until his time to take retirement aged sixty-five. He was a work rider when I got there, and was just a little way off retiring at the end of my eight years. And to tell you how long he had the job, my dad, who had ridden some horses for Italian owners when Luca had first started training twenty years ago, used to say: 'Is that guy Gozzie still there?'

For Gozzie, every work day was the Derby. Racing needs people like him. Every horse he rode got the same all-action treatment. Not all horses go sweetly along and respond to a light touch. Gozzie pushed all the way and many horses in training need just that encouragement. Most of the Gozzie types are just the same. Small, tough, little weather-beaten men. True men of Newmarket.

3 Overcoming a Crisis

It was during my time with Luca Cumani that I learnt nearly all I know about race-riding. I did have some experience in Italy, not all of it entirely helpful, and obviously the knowledge imparted by my dad was valuable, but when I got to England I was still very rough around the edges. At Luca's I picked up the finer points, and the good thing about the place was that in Stuart Jackson, the head lad, there was never a chance that you would get big-headed. Suppose I had been to the track and ridden a winner, when I got back you could bet your life that Stuart would be waiting out of sight for when I came in for evening stables to do my horses. Suddenly he'd appear and give me a massive kick up the backside to remind me that my job hadn't ended just because I'd been lucky enough to ride a winner, or a 'steering job' that anyone else could have ridden given the chance.

Being at Luca's stable was very good for me professionally.

He moved me up one step at a time. But in some ways it was always a little difficult. Luca is a very strong-minded man, and he was always very much the boss. While I was there, in the early stages of my time in the job, I was still one of the stable workers. I would come in every morning to look after my horses, feed them and ride work and then in the afternoon, go to the races. In some ways it was a help, because it would prevent you getting too big-headed, but as the relationship developed and altered neither I nor Luca knew how to handle it. Eventually, although I had everything I ever wanted, I didn't realise it and wasn't happy and I certainly was not enjoying my job.

By the time I was in my fourth year as stable jockey I felt I was being held back and that other opportunities which might have come my way were being denied me and I felt I was missing out. That was one of the reasons why I decided to accept the offer of a job in Hong Kong. The job carried the promise of a lot of money and at the time that was my reason to myself why I was taking it, but, in reality, the reason was much more the dissatisfaction with my life. I spoke about the offer to my dad, instead of to Luca, who should, I now realise, have been the first to know. When the news came out, Luca heard about it from someone else before I talked to him. I had already decided to leave, and the Hong Kong thing made it easier, but the way it came out left a bad taste. In the long run, the break between Luca and me was the best thing that could have happened at the time, but Luca was very upset and we took a long while to become friends again. For my part, though, I had been with the man, a great trainer, for eight years and learnt a great deal, around ninety per cent of what I believe I needed to become a good jockey. It would be a couple of years before I found the man who could offer that elusive missing ten per cent – John Gosden.

In between, came the most traumatic period of my life. When I left Luca, my entire concentration was on the forth-coming job in Hong Kong, but during autumn 1992 there was a lot of experimenting by young people with drugs. They were freely available in many places and, like many young people at the time, I felt some curiosity and decided to try it. One night, during that winter, I was in a club in London and bought a small quantity of cocaine. You would have to say I was naïve and, in retrospect, the fact that I was searched by the police, who found the drugs on me, was the best thing that could have happened at the time. I was not actually charged with any offence, but Hong Kong and much of the Far East has a very strict public stance on drug-taking, so the fact that I was given a police caution and the massive publicity which my being cautioned caused, was enough for the Hong Kong authorities to revoke the offer of a job there that year. The shock of that decision woke me up, made me realise I was not working at my job and that drugs were not for me. Since then I've always advised any-one who mentions drugs to keep well away from them. I also saw just how distressing that sort of newspaper and media attention can be. If the press are with you it can be great fun and very rewarding. When they want to bring you down, fairly or unfairly – this time the reports were inevitable, I suppose – their power is amazing. People in the public eye have to be whiter than white, and I've had no wish to be anything else from that point on.

During this difficult period, when the papers were doing their best to finish me off, the first person to help me was Barney Curley. I have known Barney since I was about eighteen years old. I saw a television programme and ever since then I have been fascinated by him. He was a guest in a late-night TV show called *After Dark*, on which John McCririck, the racing broadcaster, was also on the panel. The show consisted of several guests sitting round a table, and the subject was 'The Sport of Kings'. For much of the time, Barney sat very quietly, but every time he opened his mouth he made a lot of sense. He made a big impact on me. His character fascinated me. I found when I gradually got to know him that he was a very deep person. He was training about eight horses, and, just to get to know him better, I was glad to ride for him. I rode three or four of the horses, and, almost every time he asked me to ride for him, the horses won.

Barney is well known for being a shrewd operator as a trainer, but to me he was always a very nice person. He always likes to do good things for other people. So when I won a race on one of his horses, I was glad to have achieved something for him, and not let him down. It was never a question of money or even my own success. Then, in the spring of 1993, when I was at my lowest ebb, Barney was tremendously supportive. For a period of a few weeks, I was what you could call 'Zero Man'. I'd lost my confidence and was just drifting into obscurity, I suppose. Then one day Barney gave me a call. Barney is very religious, like me, and maybe that's our first real point of contact. Anyway, I went to his house, and we played snooker. Despite the publicity, I knew he felt I was a nice person.

Then we sat down and he said: 'Look, you have had the good fortune to have a God-given ability to ride horses. You must go out there and just ride. What's done is done.' Those words were the most important I'd ever heard. 'Just go out and ride', and that made me fight on. That year helped me a lot to find myself. Barney said that what happened to me had happened to thousands of other people. He made me understand that I had had too much, too early in my life. Too much achievement and too much money. The thing I thought I was looking for I already had in my hands. In those days, I never really worked at anything. All I wanted to do was wait for the weekend and party. I never worked at any aspect of my job, just went through the motions in the mornings, ate the easiest things whenever I felt hungry and never studied form – I was simply lazy. I suppose in those days, that was my reputation and I deserved it.

Money in those days was something to spend as fast as you made it. Nowadays, for me, money is a vehicle for security. Britain is a good place to live and work. For me, it's the best. No one bothers you, and the tax system, which has a maximum forty per cent deduction on even the highest earners, encourages people to play it straight. In the old days, the racing game was full of people with bags full of cash, or so the old-timers in the weighing room have told me. Now, everything is above board. The money, even presents from a winning owner, go straight into the bank, and into the official accounts. I have enough money for my needs, and now, in many ways, I am rich – not in the financial way of judging it, but now for me being rich is being happy with yourself. I can claim that, and I have the good fortune to love the job I do.

Being a believer in God came easy to a Catholic boy living in Italy. In those days, naturally, I went to church regularly. Now, I am even more sure there has to be a God. How else could the world and everything in it have been created? Different religions believe in slightly different things, but they have one thing in common: a greater being which controls everything. I also believe in life after death, and therefore try to do good in my life, to use the gift I've been given and care for other people. I ride my horses and in the meantime behave like a normal person.

When a person in the public eye is successful, inevitably he will attract attention from people for various commercial reasons. They will try to use his talents and the fact he is well known to give themselves a lift. So they use me as a ladder, just as on my way up I had to find my own ladder. The problem for someone in the public eye is where to draw the line on all the offers that are sure to come your way. Then you need to sort out the time to work, the time to play, and to be normal. Also, as you become well known, the press, which in this country seems very quick to take people up as they become established, are also ready to knock them down at the first opportunity. I believe that the press, remembering how they pushed me down during my troubles, respect me more for getting back on top.

When the door to Hong Kong closed, at least I still had the option to prove myself in the big arena of English racing. This time, though, I had to roll up my sleeves and start again from scratch with no safe job in a big stable to make things easier for me. Luckily, at the start of 1993, I bumped into another young guy who had something to prove. David Loder had just begun training in the Sefton Lodge stables, which had been the base for Charles St George's horses which Henry Cecil trained for him. The St George string operated virtually as a self-contained unit. Sadly, in 1992, Charles St George had died and his brother Edward, who lives in the Bahamas, where he runs the Grand Bahama Port Authority with Sir Jack Hayward, the owner of Wolverhampton Wanderers, took over.

Edward St George decided to operate the stable independently of Henry Cecil, and, in the autumn of 1992, he appointed David Loder, who had been assistant trainer with Geoff Wragg, as trainer of his family horses. David's family had had a long involvement with racing ownership and breeding and his cousin Edmund bred and raced the brilliant fillies Marwell and Marling. Like me, when 1993 started, David had something to prove, and he and I teamed up. Both of us were hungry for winners. To that extent we used each other. The winners began to flow. I was on my way back and David was starting his very quick rise towards the top of the training profession. In spring 1993, too, I had plenty to thank Ian Balding for. Especially his great mare Lochsong, who was making her own strides towards the top of her tree. Gradually, thanks to Ian and David and many other small stables which also helped me, my rehabilitation began and when at the end of the year John Gosden took me on as stable jockey it was pretty much complete.

Apart from his friendship, I will always have a debt to Barney Curley because it was he who first introduced me to John. I did know him slightly, but Barney made me wait for the right time before he introduced us properly. We had a chat and at the end of 1993, I was lucky to be appointed to the job of stable jockey. Even that did not go totally smoothly. We had a brief chat at the end of September, but somehow the news got out. That was unfortunate because at the time Michael (Muis) Roberts was the official jockey for Sheikh Mohammed, having taken over the job when Steve Cauthen had retired from riding and had gone back to America. We hadn't settled anything, but, obviously, John was Sheikh Mohammed's principal trainer, and when it came out that I would be joining John's stable, it was embarrassing for Muis Roberts.

Of all the people I have met in racing, John Gosden is the most straightforward. He is always to the point, and allows you the chance to stretch yourself to the limit. In racing, with many other people it's 'me, me, me' all the time. The difference with John is that he wants you to do well, to achieve something for yourself. If you do well, he's pleased for you. It's only in England, in my experience, that that happens in the jockeys' room. I think it's because racing in England is like a very big pie, and for the leading jockeys there's plenty of pie to go round. In other countries, when someone wins the Derby everyone else hates them as there may be few other big races where they can catch up. The saying goes, 'Racing tames lions', but here I think we jockeys at least share each other's successes and enjoy them.

When I first got the job with John, he told me he wanted me to achieve something; to become champion jockey. He told me he would not tie me down, that if his stable had one horse going to Carlisle and I could ride four outside favourites the same day at Kempton, I could stay in the south. I knew I would need all the help I could get and John said he would not stand in my way in those circumstances. John looks at both sides of the coin and decides what's best for everyone. He's not selfish, so I've been very lucky to work with him.

After the first season, he also helped introduce me to the Godolphin operation of Sheikh Mohammed, which has had such a beneficial effect on my career. Knowing John has given me that extra ten per cent I was looking for, if I had known I was looking for it, that is. Nowadays, I realise that life is not just riding horses. That extra factor is peace of mind, and now, riding good horses and living a rewarding life, I'm the happiest man in the world. I'm in control of my life, and with John as your boss, you are also in control of the horses. He allows you to do what you want on a horse and make the split-second decisions you think will make the difference in riding a race. That freedom in your job is everything for a jockey.

Every day of my life, I had wanted to work for Sheikh Mohammed. He had 450 horses in training, a huge monster of an operation. Steve Cauthen held down the job of stable jockey for two years, Michael Roberts for just one season, and they found dealing with thirty different trainers an impossible situation. I always wondered whether working for Sheikh Mohammed would eat you alive. But John organised things so that while I was Sheikh Mohammed's jockey, the contract was really with his stable. To do things that way, John was putting his head on the line. Look at it from his viewpoint: he was putting up this boy, even though he didn't really know me. Even if he saw that I had changed from how I was a year before, he had everything to lose if things went wrong. But he just said: 'I'll back you up, it's all in your hands.'

His saying that made me more determined to pay him back, to show his confidence in me was not a mistake, that it was the correct decision that he had made. It was just the extra stimulation I needed to prove myself.

At the end of the season, having come second in the jockeys' championship with 149 winners, I took a two-week break in Italy. In the meantime, I'd met Catherine and we were going out together by then, but as part of my preparation for the following year I went on from Italy to Morocco, and didn't take Catherine with me, just a Walkman, ten tapes and went into virtual isolation. I started to listen to my dad. He and my stepmother were also there, but I was so focused, so inside myself, that apart from listening to some excellent advice from him, I was a real loner.

He emphasised just how crucial it would be to get to my

lowest weight before the start of the season. He said, 'If you do that and from the beginning have no weight worries, you can concentrate properly on what you have to do.' He said my mind would be right and that there would be one less thing to worry about.

Talking to Dad and also before the holiday to John, we realised that we could take advantage of what amounted to a loophole. I was very keen to improve on my second place and become champion for the first time. With John and Sheikh Mohammed, as well as my other loyal stables to back me up, I thought I had a chance, and reckoned that if I rode the entire all-weather season in January and February, I could get a big start on Pat Eddery and the other jockeys of the old school who never rode on the sand tracks. I felt I had something to prove to myself, my dad and John.

I would get back from Morocco on 31 December, ready to ride on New Year's Day, and hoping that by working hard I could get a flying start of maybe twenty winners before Pat and the others got going. So back in Morocco I lived the life of a hermit. In the morning I would get up and have a single cup of coffee. In the afternoon I would drink a bottle of Evian water and then every day go to the local market. I'd buy a big fish, grill it and eat it for dinner. Then, at night, I would go out and walk the beach alone with my tapes and my Walkman. I'd talk to myself, hardly at all to my parents. By the end of the time, my weight was down to 8st 1lb, my lightest for more than five years. I had my hair cut short. The whole idea was to create a new image of myself, and with my new look, short hair and gaunt, sun-tanned face, I looked older and meaner, as I had intended. But the image was for myself – for me to see when I looked in the mirror every day – to remind me to do things differently, to behave differently outwardly and inside myself. I was a man with a mission, and the new look would remind me how vital it was I remembered it. We decided, John, my dad and me, that I would not talk to the press, no interviews, just try to prove myself.

At the start of the all-weather, apart from hoping for about twenty winners, I didn't really have a target. I had met Catherine the previous September, and was certain I would eventually marry her. But in January 1994 I had to be brutal and unkind. I said, 'I'm very sorry, let me go out there and work. I'm not trying to be nasty, but I've no time for you. If I do this to the best of my ability, it will make a difference to our lives for the next forty years.' She agreed, and I did 'go out there and just ride', as Barney would have me do, and by the start of the turf season I had fifty-one winners and it was almost wrapped up before we started.

Needless to say, there were people trying to whip up a controversy, saying the winners should not count towards the title. The situation hadn't occurred before because when it was Steve Cauthen or Pat Eddery or Muis Roberts or Willie Carson, none of them ever got involved on the all-weather, which in those days was not so extensive anyway. My view was that I'd earned every one of those fifty-one winners, working my butt off in the freezing cold at Wolverhampton, Southwell and Lingfield. It was bloody hard work, nothing more or less. I was just like the other guys who have to keep going every year on the all-weather, picking up what the big boys leave them. One Saturday, I remember I had five rides in the afternoon at Lingfield, and then had to drive like a maniac for the seven o'clock start at the Wolverhampton floodlit meeting, where I had five more rides. Wolverhampton is great, with its lovely, warm, glass-fronted restaurant where the punters spend a pleasant

Saturday night betting, eating and drinking. Meanwhile, beyond the glass and in the cold, the temperature, including wind-chill, was reckoned to be ten degrees below freezing, and there we were – me, my friend Jason Weaver, Jimmy Quinn, Lindsay Charnock, Tony Clark and the rest of us – all trying to win a percentage of six little £2,000 races.

So right through January and February of 1994, I kept a pledge to myself: to stay hard and lean, to work, and, with the help of Matty, my agent, to get the rides I needed to give me that edge in the race for the title, while Pat Eddery and the others were still enjoying their regular winter break. I was determined also to keep another pledge, and therefore stayed firmly with the idea of not talking to the press. The coverage a year earlier had been so distressing that I wanted to prove a point. Even when the winners started to come, as they did with ever-increasing regularity, I thought, 'Suppose I came off a horse and broke a leg, they would all be calling me a loser again.' I felt that as long as I kept remote and no one could get close, I would be able to get on with it. At the end of the all-weather programme in early March, my dad and stepmother came to stay with me for the whole of the spring and summer.

The fact that they were there was obviously a help. I didn't have to worry much about normal things. The house was looked after and my meals were prepared for me. All I had to do was keep fit and get ready to do my job. It must have been very hard for my parents. Probably, I was trying too hard with my riding and it was not much fun for them. Because my dad was a champion jockey and able to go and watch the races every day in the betting shop in the town, we soon got to analysing every ride. Every race I lost, I felt I had made a mistake and that used to daunt me. I believed that I needed every winner possible if I was to become champion. One lost race could make all the difference. My dad had the same attitude. So, as I said, he would go and watch every one of my rides and, if he reckoned I'd given a horse a bad ride, that night we would argue about it for one and a half hours or more. There was no escape. He was a champion jockey for thirty years and is the one person in the world that I could not bullshit. He was my dad, too.

For all that, the summer came and went, and the parents went back to Italy. All the time I was stretching my lead over Jason Weaver, who had also got going on the all-weather, back in those freezing winter days. By 1 September I had already reached 200 for the year and, with the title already just about guaranteed, there was even talk that I would break Sir Gordon Richards's record of 269 in a year. I knew, however, that this would not be possible, as my winning opportunities were beginning to dry up, and, with very little all-weather racing to come after November, there were just about eight weeks left. So, Sir Gordon was safe, but I did have my eyes on another great champion's record, and this time it was the score of 229.

And the name of this particular record holder? No, it wasn't Piggott, who never actually got to 200 in a season, or Eddery, or Carson. The name was Gianfranco Dettori, multiple champion in Italy. Anyway, with 200 by 1 September it should have been a cinch, but as is liable to happen when the meetings thin out in the early autumn, I hit a really quiet spell. The good rides were harder to come by and it became a question of working even harder, grinding out the winners one at a time. I got to the required figure of 230 by 19 October and by then I knew that the Richards record was well out of reach. It's just as well it was, for by then I was gone, physically and mentally drained. I was going out to the track every day to ride horses because I had to. The relief of getting to 230 and beating the Old Man was immense. I realised straight away that I couldn't manage another step. Already I'd had more than 1,000 rides and wanted to quit there and then.

All year, my dad had been pushing me to the limit. Now I was at the top and couldn't get any further, so I spoke to him. He told me to take a step back, and I decided that because I had a strong book of rides already arranged for the Breeders' Cup meeting in Churchill Downs, Kentucky, the following month, it would be sensible to take a fortnight off, and then go out to the Breeders' Cup a few days early. It turned out to be the best career decision in my life. I arrived in Louisville, Kentucky, birthplace of the great heavyweight boxing champion Muhammad Ali, a few days before the meeting and was able to ride track work on Lochsong, the great sprint mare, Barathea, Only Royale and Belle Genius. They were all great rides and I had taken advantage of my nice rest to be prepared for one big, final effort.

One of the best things to come from the 1994 season was my association with Lochsong. Her trainer Ian Balding had been one of the first, with David Loder, to show his confidence in me the previous year when events had been going against me, and by the following year, when she was a six-year-old, she was assuredly the favourite racehorse in Britain. Considering that the public are generally quicker to appreciate the best jump horses, as they are around for much longer, this affection for Lochsong was unusual. For a sprinter, as far as I can recall, and from what other jockeys and people in racing tell me, this public affection was unique.

It is easy to understand the appeal of Lochsong. She had the most amazing speed and at five furlongs you only had to point her in the direction of the winning post, and, in her prime, at five and six, she would do the rest. At six furlongs, she was vulnerable, especially if, as sometimes happened, she went to post too free. By the time she got to the starting gate, her race would sometimes be run, and on the way back the last furlong would seem like a mile. So she was in some ways a flawed genius, but the flaws were worth putting up with along with the ecstasy of her best days. As I said after one of her best days, 'She's like Linford Christie without the lunch-box.' Sorry, Linford, but she was certainly a gold-medal performer, even if destiny would not smile on her in racing's Olympics, the Breeders' Cup.

By November 1994, though, her fame and prestige could hardly have been higher. She broke the Newmarket five furlong record by half a second in the Palace House Stakes; easily won Sandown's Temple Stakes, and the King's Stand Stakes at Royal Ascot was virtually a trap-to-line exhibition. The other side of the coin, however, were her 'bolting going to the start' runs in the July Cup at Newmarket and the Nunthorpe at York. By the time we went to Longchamp – she won between the two disappointments at Goodwood – there were those who reckoned she was as temperamental as she was talented. Anyone at Longchamp for the Prix de l'Abbaye that year went home with a different picture. This time, thanks to the co-operation of the understanding French stewards, Lochsong was allowed to walk to the start, saving all that precious energy for the race itself. We exploded from the stalls, came up the middle of the track and the first I saw of any other horse was when we pulled up, apart from a crafty peep which told me we were five lengths clear of the best sprinters in Europe.

And so to Churchill Downs. The test would be severe, in that the Americans go flat out from the start, but also as it was to be on dirt and round a turn, both totally unusual for Lochsong. It was a sporting challenge by Ian and Lochsong's owner-breeder Jeff Smith, and when Lochsong warmed up with her now famous three-furlong work a couple of days before the Breeders' Cup Sprint, she had the locals checking their clocks to see if they had stopped. Lochsong covered that distance around a bend in thirty-three seconds, and when she trailed home in the actual race, finishing tailed off, having chipped a bone in her knee, I had to wonder whether that flying spin had caused it. Still, my other three rides were all good prospects: Barathea, winner of the Irish 2,000 Guineas and the Queen Anne Stakes at Royal Ascot, was going for the Mile; Belle Genius in the Juvenile Fillies had previously won the Moyglare Stakes in Ireland; and Only Royale, who ran in the Turf race, had been just about the easiest winner of the year when she'd run away with the Yorkshire Oaks at York.

They all ran well. Belle Genius, showing that Paul Kelleway, her trainer, knew what it took to challenge the best horses in the world, ran a great third in the Juvenile Fillies race behind the flying pair Flanders and Serena's Song. Injury did not enable Flanders's career to develop but two seasons later Serena's Song was still racking up the dollars in Group 1 company. Only Royale did not disgrace herself, finishing fifth behind Tikkanen in the Turf race, but the best result was her trainer's, Luca Cumani's, other challenger, Barathea. To win the race for Britain and Europe would always be important, but, at that time, European jockeys were getting a bad press in the United States. The owners and trainers there seemed to believe that our jockeys could not match their best riders on their tracks. When you think of it, that made no sense. I would say that American tracks are the easiest to ride. They are all the same shape, oval, and most are little more than a mile round. There is the odd exception, like Belmont Park, New York, where the dirt track is, by American standards, very big. True, things sometimes change when it rains and you get differences in the surface, but, as I said, the tracks over there are easy to ride.

So when Barathea won I was doubly delighted. It is not often that you win a race with a purse of two million dollars and a first prize of more than a million. But it wasn't the prize money or the importance of the occasion which most pleased me. It was the knowledge that I had made a point on behalf of my friends and colleagues in the weighing rooms up and down the country. A country in which the tracks are so different and you have to get to know them all. Their ups and downs; whether they are right- or left-handed. Where the best ground usually is. On which course you can ride a waiting race. On which ones it's better to be up near the leaders or ride from the front. We believe we are the most versatile jockeys in the world, so to win in America you really only need to have the right horse. That year at Churchill Downs I had the tools to do the job and the job got done.

There was also the point for me that for the first time I was going to another country as the champion jockey of the country in which I live and work. I am an Italian, but my home now is England. It's the place I enjoy working in. Ask any of the famous jockeys around the world where they would like to go to prove themselves and if they are being honest they will all tell you 'England'. It's a great country to live in, and horse racing in England has far more prestige than in almost any other country. Television coverage on the major networks is exceptional compared with France, America and even Ireland, and the public in England care as much about the horses as they do about who won and at what odds. After Barathea won there was a whole range of emotions for me, all of them positive. For me, 1994 had been a fantastic year. There was achievement and also the feeling of pride that I had been able to give something back to the people who had shown so much faith in me – especially to John Gosden. But then, of course, we had come to the end of the year of my first championship. To prove it was no fluke, I would have to do it all over again the next year.

4 Champion Jockey

The start of the 1995 season for me was much more relaxed than the previous year. Naturally, I was happy to begin the year as champion, but it soon became obvious that there would be a battle between Jason Weaver and me for the title. We were both ready for action from the start of the all-weather season, and planned to go right down to the wire in November. We had been good friends for a long time and I felt I could always relate to him. We were both at Luca Cumani's as apprentices. He came there a couple of years after me. He's a year younger, but I always believed he was doing all the right things, and I tried to offer him my best advice as we were making it towards the top together.

But in 1995, for the first time, we began to clash. We had always been good friends, but now the media attention on what everyone thought would become a championship battle between us started to have an effect. Friends and parents were pushing us both to the limit and we started to get in each other's way. Like me, he had ridden more than 200 winners the year before, his first year with Mark Johnston's powerful Yorkshire stable, but now he would be in the mainstream in Newmarket.

I suppose our conflict began when Jason got his job riding for David Loder. Like me, when I rode for David's stable in 1993, Jason had no contract, but at the beginning of the year he had the ride on all the horses at Sefton Lodge. Horses that, the year before, I would have been able to ride were now being ridden by Jason, who was pleased to stay in the south and ride at all the big meetings. This suited him much better than the previous year when, it seemed, he often had to travel north from his home in Newmarket when the rest of us were running in big races. You can imagine how disappointed he used to get when he had to go 200 miles north for a couple of rides in small races, when the biggest prizes were on offer a mile or two from his home in Newmarket.

The conflict started on the all-weather. David ran some of his horses as usual in February and Jason made a good start to the season. Like me the year before, he worked very hard and his stables were in good form. So he won plenty of races, and for the first time in his life found himself in front of me, rather than pressing up from behind. I was a little upset about that, I suppose, and Jason started to make a couple of jokes about it. Things went on from that. I see now that I was sour about it and Jason got sour, too. Before that we had a great friendship. Now the sourness, probably made worse by the attitude of everyone around us, especially the press, but also family and friends, spoilt our friendship.

So, to cut a long story short, we had a fall-out. When I look back, I can see I was feeling nasty in a childish way about him. I'd watch out for his rides, whether we were riding together or at different meetings. If he didn't have a winner during the day, I'd think, 'Great.' If he did, I'd be miserable. I was not living my own life. I was living it through him and his successes or failures. For about six weeks I was feeling really hurt. A year later, I was able to look back and had to admit it wasn't Jason's fault. But then it probably wasn't mine either. There was definitely a case of the press wanting to make us jealous of each other. The split between us was totally out of character. Then Jason lost the job with David Loder, and at the same time my stables started to get going. I also got back some of the rides for David.

Without quite matching the score of the previous year, I was able to retain the championship, but when I sat down and thought about the business with Jason I realised how stupid it had been. We sat down together and sorted it out. We agreed we had both been silly. Why had we fallen out? Only for a silly old championship. Friendship is worth more. It was a good lesson for both of us. The price of success.

Friendship means a lot to me. Many of the jockeys are good friends, and with the success I have enjoyed I realise how lucky I am in my life. When I was younger, not working very hard with my job, I had no idea what I wanted. Now I want nothing to change. If anything, I have too much of everything. My job is very satisfying: riding good horses for nice people who understand the animals. And my personal life is marvellous. I am one of those lucky people who knew when I had met the person with whom I wanted to spend the rest of my life.

Catherine, my fiancée, is from a racing family, as her father Twink Allen is an expert in the horse breeding industry. Catherine is reading for her degree but as she has always ridden she also enjoys riding out in the morning. I had noticed her while I was at David Loder's, as she worked there for a couple of months during her holidays. One day, Catherine took a filly to run in a race at Haydock and I was riding the filly. I was not in a good mood as the filly was carrying 8st 4lb, which is my absolute minimum, so I felt quite grumpy. The only thing to cheer me up was seeing Catherine leading up the filly. As she held the filly while I got up in the paddock, I asked her, 'Can I take you out for a date?' She didn't answer, so I said, 'Give me your phone number.' Catherine said, 'You won't remember it anyway.' But she still told me. So we went out for the race and when I came back after the race I repeated the number correctly. So we arranged to go out to the pictures. I must say I was very nervous. It was during the time when I was being most hard on myself, trying to sort things out and I hadn't had a girlfriend for a year. So we went to a cinema in Cambridge. I went to pick her up and Catherine was wearing bright pink lipstick. Outside of racing I'd never met the girl, yet I said, 'I don't like girls with make-up.' She didn't say anything then, but she hasn't worn any make-up since. She says she didn't usually wear any anyway.

I thought it would probably not be easy retaining my championship, but it didn't take long to see that the ammunition I had to call on was going to enable me to win some pretty big races in the 1995 season. The Godolphin team came back to England in brilliant shape, and with Moonshell as my ride in the 1,000 Guineas, I knew she could be anything. Godolphin have their horses in work in Dubai right until the time they fill up the planes to England with the animals, their grooms for the journey, and all the equipment they need. Another part of the stable staff is sent

The two great loves of my life.

My great friend, John Gosden, at breakfast.

Another early morning start.

Two key players in the Dettori team:
my valet, Dave Curry (above),
and my agent, Matty Cowing (below).

At Stanley House Stables.

Schooling a David Loder filly at Newmarket.

Derek Thompson cracks a joke at Sandown.

Collecting money for the Centre of Riding Therapy from
Peter Walwyn, Lady Howard de Walden and Lord Howard de Walden.

Riding out.

Relaxing at home with Catherine.

ahead to England to make sure their new accommodation is ready when they step off the planes. It's important that everything is right, because there's no time for any mistakes. Within a day or so of arriving, the 1,000 Guineas is on us and the horses have to be ready.

Some cold winters in England in recent years have left trainers tearing their hair out in frustration. It's a delicate balance to time a horse's preparation for a big race. If on the day the trainer wants to work his horse in a serious Classic gallop it has been raining hard and the ground is too soft, or if winter drags on too long and it leaves the horses with shaggy coats, they will probably not be able to show their best form. Fillies, especially, can suffer in that way in a cold English winter and when the horses came into the paddock for the 1,000 Guineas of 1995 Moonshell's coat, bursting with the healthy sheen that weeks of warm sun had given it, stood out against some of the others. She had raced only once before as a two-year-old for the Henry Cecil stable, and won a maiden race nicely, but it was going to be a big step from a maiden race to a Classic, with a mile probably short of her ideal trip.

Moonshell ran a great race, coming in third. When we came back afterwards, the family – she was in the joint-ownership of Sheikh Maktoum Al-Maktoum, the ruler of Dubai, and Godolphin, run by his brother Sheikh Mohammed – was very happy. Naturally, that was because the winner, Harayir, ridden by Richard Hills, is owned by another brother, Sheikh Hamdan. He rode her because Willie Carson, Sheikh Hamdan's first jockey, chose Aqaarid instead. She was second and that made it a clear sweep for the Maktoum family. We were just as happy as we all knew Moonshell's chance would come when she went a mile and a half for the Oaks. The Godolphin magic, which we'd seen the year before with my great favourite Balanchine, who'd won the Epsom Oaks and Irish Derby, was still working, luckily for me!

I didn't have a ride in the 2,000 Guineas, so missed out on the first two English Classic races of the year, but if I had been able to look into a crystal ball I would not have been able to believe my eyes. I was to win twelve Group 1 races in Europe during the year. Considering there are only seventy-three of these in Europe's major racing countries – Great Britain, France, Ireland, Italy and Germany – this was to be an unbelievable year, especially when, as an English-based jockey, I was to win six of the twenty-five Group 1 races in France. I'd already won my first: I had been delighted when, at Longchamp in late April, the five-year-old, Pelder, had been a very easy winner for his owner, my compatriot Osvaldo Pedroni.

Pelder was originally trained in Italy, but was switched to Newmarket into the care of Paul Kelleway. Some people find Paul's nickname, Pattern-race Paul, amusing, but he earned it with his many wins in major races, despite always having a small team in his yard, a few steps down the road from John Gosden's stable on Bury Road. Pelder is a horse who had to have soft ground, and when he got it he was a match for anything. He got the mud that day in Paris and beat the champion hurdler Alderbrook, by then back with Julie Cecil after his winter with Kim Bailey, by three lengths. Some hot French horses were behind that day and Freedom Cry, a horse I would encounter another day on the same Longchamp track, made the form look very solid.

I had to wait only a week after the two English Guineas races for my next classic, and therefore Group 1 win, and again it was at Longchamp. I was to ride a horse whose name should have given someone the idea of writing a poem, something like:

> A jockey called Frankie Dettori,
> Won a French classic race on Vettori,
> It sounded strange at the time, that their names made
> a rhyme,
> But I tell you, it is a true story.

Perhaps it's as well that nobody did!

Vettori was not the best Classic winner I'll ever ride, but he took his chance to beat the best horses that the French trainers could put out against him. In the end, we beat Atticus, a horse with a big reputation trained by the brilliant Criquette Head, with the rest nowhere. The Godolphin knack at winning first time out was also still working. John's horses, too, were flying at this stage, and, the same afternoon at Longchamp, we won another Group 1 together, with Flemensfirth, owned by Sheikh Mohammed. John had a great spring, and we were back in France again the weekend before the Epsom Derby meeting, with Flemensfirth once more, this time in the Prix du Jockey Club, the French equivalent of the Derby. This was a tougher test for Flemensfirth and he ran a good race, but was only fifth this time. Still, it wasn't too bad, with the much-hyped Celtic Swing, the champion two-year-old of 1994, winning, Winged Love, next time out the winner of the Irish Derby, in third, and none other than Classic Cliché, of whom more later, in fourth. The day was not unfruitful, though, as we won the Prix Jean Prat over nine furlongs with John's Torrential, another Sheikh Mohammed horse.

My own tally of winners in ordinary races was also going quite nicely by this time, and I was in great shape as I went out to ride Moonshell in the Oaks at Epsom five days later. Willie Carson was again on Aqaarid and she was favourite even though her stamina was less certain than Moonshell's.

In the race it was no contest between them, but the two Michael Stoute fillies Dance A Dream and Pure Grain made us work for the big prize. Moonshell would not be denied and won nicely by a little more than a length. The Maktoum family have an amazing record in the Oaks, but for the relatively small Godolphin team to win for the second time in a row was fantastic. I was delighted to win and delighted for everyone in the team as I came back. Twenty-four hours later, the same mile and a half at Epsom brought a different reaction from me to a Godolphin win. I was glad for them that Lammtarra won, but I'd rather he'd have let Tamure and me stay ahead for the last few yards instead of flying past as he did just when I thought I'd won the Derby.

Some jockeys wait a lifetime for the one big horse. For me, in a few short years, I can point to Lochsong, the fastest horse on four legs in my opinion, and the unbeaten Lammtarra, as horses associated with me. As I just mentioned, Lammtarra had spoiled my Derby party, giving Walter Swinburn another win in England's most important race. The previous year Lammtarra had won his only race as a two-year-old, for the late Alex Scott, so tragically murdered by an employee just when his career was taking off. Lammtarra went to Dubai to join Godolphin and had some niggling problems before coming back to England, where the Derby probably seemed an impossible quest. The first thing I remember about Lammtarra was when Walter Swinburn rode him one morning in a gallop at Newmarket against me on Vettori, my French 2,000 Guineas winner. The gallop was staged two weeks before the 1995 Derby and, while Vettori was a good miler, I thought Lammtarra would need to win by more than a mere neck that day in order to have a chance in the Derby so soon after. I would have called the gallop 'workmanlike', but Sheikh Mohammed, who watched the work, said: 'Run him in the Derby.' I was shocked and thought, 'You're mad.' How could they run in the Derby a horse which had not yet run that season and which had run just once as a two-year-old and then had had a serious health problem during the winter in Dubai and had suffered disruption to his training programme. When it was confirmed Lammtarra would run, I thought: 'They've definitely gone mad.'

As I said earlier, I was on Tamure for John and we were very hopeful that he could win. Tamure was unbeaten until then, having won the Sandown Classic Trial last time out, and we felt he had a really good chance. For me, the race went absolutely to plan, spot-on, and I made my ground exactly where I wanted to. I hit the front in the last 100 yards, only for Lammtarra to catch me fifty yards out and beat me by a length. I shouted 'You bastard', but then immediately thought back to the gallop and Sheikh Mohammed. 'The Boss is always right – that's one thing you have to learn in life,' I said to myself, and it's not far from the truth. The result was very hard for me to swallow, though, but you never know what can happen, and little did I expect that next time out it would be me that had the good fortune to get the ride on him.

At the time it was offered, of course, it was a nice feeling to get the ride, and when I was asked, I accepted like a shot. But then when I thought about it, I reckoned I was in a no-win situation. I thought, 'What if he gets beat, they will all be saying "Walter would have won on him".' Luckily for me, when the news that I had the ride was announced, I was having a four-day break in Sardinia. I came back on the Friday, the day before the race, and until the race I hadn't sat on him. Because of the way he'd won at Epsom, many people were regarding Lammtarra as a speed horse, but I had been studying the video of the Derby and reckoned he needed a couple of furlongs to wind up and get into his stride. I thought that Ascot's short straight and the horse's inexperience might be a problem, but, as everyone knows, Lammtarra won.

Everyone in racing, especially in English racing, has the same ambition. There are three races to win, the Epsom Derby, the King George and the Arc – and Lammtarra achieved all three before I did! At Ascot we were drawn on the outside. The King George is a race where it's easy to find trouble, especially on the rails, but from our position we were able to keep galloping. I decided to make my move at the three-furlong pole. Lammtarra was one of the first off the bridle but then I had just got him going when I could feel this monster coming through – that great buzz. I'd been rowing away and then I got a bump and was knocked wide. Just for a second I even forgot about Pentire, but then I looked to my left and saw him. Just as a racing car driver looks at the line at the end of every lap trying to cut a few milliseconds from his time, entering the straight I tried to pinch a few inches.

I looked at the reins on Pentire and saw they were really tight. I thought, 'I have to get him off the bridle', so I asked him to give me another gear. Then Michael Hills had to ask Pentire to go as a response and he got a neck in front. But then Lammtarra fought back and showed that determin-ation which sets the champion apart. The race was like a boxing match, Lammtarra being the true prize fighter. Unlike some of the other talented horses you get to ride, Lammtarra could take a punch and then come back with his own knock-out blow.

And so to the Arc and the final challenge. In my mind,

until the Arc I had only paid back half of the hurt which losing the Derby had meant to me. The Arc would complete the consolation for me. Catherine does not come away racing with me very often but this time we spent a long weekend in Paris. I had a couple of rides at Longchamp on the Saturday and Lammtarra was to be the highlight on the Sunday, Arc day. I rode two Group-race winners, Flemensfirth in the Prix Dollar for John and Grey Shot (Prix de Lutece) for Ian Balding, from my three rides on the Saturday and we were all in a great mood when we went back early to the Georges V, a beautiful old-fashioned hotel right in the centre of town. That night, rather than stay in the hotel, we decided to go out and see the show at the Crazy Horse, where we had dinner.

The next morning I got up at nine o'clock and started getting ready at nine thirty. I knew the traffic is always bad in Paris on Arc day and I was anxious not to be late. By the time Catherine was organised, at eleven, I was 'walking the box', and I insisted we went then. On the way to the Bois de Boulogne there was hardly a car in sight, and when we arrived at eleven thirty, not even the gatemen were in place. You can tell I was not my normal pleasant self when I admit that when Catherine asked me to get her a badge, I said: 'Get your own badge, I'm working!' I can understand why she might not have been that delighted with me while she waited the three hours for the first race after that performance from me.

For me, though, the early arrival at Longchamp was just the thing I needed to take away my nerves. In the jockeys' room I at last began to relax. I had a couple of races to ride in before the Arc and that also helped. When we went out for the big race all I needed to do was to remind myself that Longchamp can be a very difficult track to ride. My requirement was to make sure I kept out of trouble. The Godolphin–Sheikh Mohammed team planned everything to perfection, and in Luso, owned by the Sheikh's great friend Saeed Manana, they shrewdly found the perfect pacemaker. More importantly, nobody else was entirely aware that Luso was fulfilling that role. I was able to take a prominent position behind Luso as Lammtarra jumped off well from out of the gate. Everything went to plan and I waited to let him see the straight and what he had to do. Then I got hold of him, and said, 'Let's go.' I wanted to kill them off. In the paddock beforehand, Sheikh Mohammed had said, 'Be handy. It's up to you to make the most of it.' By then I'd ridden Lammtarra a few times, at home as well as at Ascot, and knew that he stayed really well and was a great fighter. So when we kicked I knew that the others would have to use their speed to get to me. Then, when they did get to my quarters, they had to try to contend with his fighting spirit. I remember seeing Freedom Cry coming up to my horse's quarters and wondering whether we had enough petrol left in the tank. We did and Lammtarra was going away again at the line. It was to be the last race of his career, and he there-fore remained unbeaten, the first European champion to do so since Ribot, a horse from the 1950s that was a great favourite of my father's, as he was Italian owned, trained and bred.

As we crossed the line, everything seemed to stop and to my mind it all went dark. It was the reaction of being able to ease off and stop concentrating, I suppose, but I remem-ber standing up on the horse and looking across at the huge, packed grandstands. For a few seconds I was in a kind of shock, almost trance-like, but then, just as quickly, woke up to the enormity of the moment. I came back and jumped off the horse, in my then-normal Angel Cordero style, and participated in the presentation in front of the winning post. Sheikh Mohammed and his family and friends were all there and when it came to my turn to collect my own trophy it was a wonderful moment.

When the presentation finished, I could not contain myself any longer and, holding the cup in my left hand, ran right along the front of the grandstands at top speed and into the exit from the track to the paddock, doing high (or in my case, quite low) fives to every hand that was presented to me. On either side of the exit the crowds were lined, tightly packed, and by this time I was more like a dervish than a jockey. Starting on the right, I slapped all the hands I could reach, still galloping at Lammtarra pace, and then halfway through it, changed the cup to my right hand, and veered across to the left before going into the paddock for the post-race interviews. The funniest thing for me during the presentation was the sound of the British national anthem being played to salute the success of a horse bred in the United States, trained and owned by Dubaians and ridden by an Italian. If nothing else, it showed how international racing in Britain has become.

As I was saying before I was so rudely (at first) and then so beautifully (the next two times) interrupted by Lammtarra, the Oaks was great for me. To win the classic again for the team showed we were doing everything right. Sheikh Mohammed wanted to win the big ones with Godolphin and we were doing it. I had a nice win in the King's Stand Stakes on Godolphin's So Factual, who came late and fast to catch Lake Coniston, then reckoned to be the next champion sprinter. Unfortunately, the King's Stand, while still the top sprint race at Royal Ascot, is no longer a Group 1, and is now a Group 2 race. Lammtarra's King George was my next Group 1 win, but before I got another there was the pain and shock of that terrible fall at Haydock in early August when we lost a faithful old servant of John's, Wainwright.

That accident killed Wainwright and I was laid out on the track for quite a while. Happily for me, I was able to make a pretty quick comeback at the big York meeting, and again it was So Factual who kept my run going, with an easy win in the Nunthorpe Stakes.

In recent years, the Maktoum family have been having a number of horses trained in Germany, and one horse I rode with some success in that country was Germany, a four-year-old trained by Bruno Schutz, and owned by Mr Jaber Abdullah, one of the close friends of the family. He won two Group 1s, first in Munich, and then the Grosser Preis von Baden at the pretty track of Baden-Baden, which stages some great racing, especially in late summer. The ground was soft that day at Baden-Baden and Germany was able to show himself a high-class performer, winning by five lengths. There were some good English horses a long way behind that day.

Now, though, it was back home with thoughts of another Classic win, as I had been looking forward to riding John's nice horse Presenting in the St Leger, the last Classic race of the season. Presenting was the ante-post favourite, but it began to look as if I would be snookered anyway, as Godolphin were planning to let Classic Cliché take his chance in the race, which meant I would be claimed to ride him. Unluckily for John and Presenting's owner George Strawbridge, who breeds some lovely horses in the USA, the rain started to come down at Doncaster and there was no option but to withdraw Presenting, who must have fast ground to show his best form. Luckily for me, though, I had Classic Cliché to ride. He had been running well in some top races over a mile and a half, just getting outpaced at the crucial time by Pentire in the King Edward at Royal Ascot, and then in the Irish Derby where he was a close fifth. Both times, though, he was running on and while lots of people were asking, 'How can a horse by Salse win a St Leger?' I was in no doubt he'd stay the trip well.

I didn't realise when I went to Doncaster that day that I needed two wins to reach my 1,000 winners in England. The race before the St Leger made it 999, as I won on a nice handicapper of Bryan McMahon's called Band On The Run. Then it was the big race and the possibility that I had timed it to win my thousandth race in a Classic. In the race I rode the horse as I believed he should be ridden, never doubting his stamina. From the start we were always going easily, and early in the straight we went on. I asked for his effort two out and we went clear, galloping really strongly. We'd won another Classic, the fourth in a row for Godolphin and my third of the year in England, and the reception as I came in was tremendous. Like a great big party. The St Leger, which is the oldest Classic race, has an added attraction for the winning jockey and the public: the famous hat with St Leger written on it, which is placed on the winning jockey's head. I'd wanted to win that ever since I'd come to England, and now it's the most treasured item in my trophy cabinet. When they gave me that it was a bit like getting an international cap for football. As the hat was presented, I saw a bottle of champagne which had been left on the table. I quickly opened the bottle, and sprayed every-one around with it. Now I know what it's like to win a Grand Prix race!

So I'd got to 1,000 winners and won three classic races in England in a single season and was still only twenty-four. But then I still had a few to go to catch my dad. Around 2,800, I think!

Meanwhile, John was still flying, especially where major races were concerned, and only a week after the St Leger another day trip to Longchamp brought another big double. John's two-year-old Lord Of Men had been going well as he'd gained experience and won a couple of nice races at home. John decided it was time for him to step up in grade and aimed him at the Prix de la Salamandre, one of the three most important races in the French calendar. André Fabre's Barricade was the favourite and we were pretty unfancied by the betting public as 6–1 fifth favourite in a field of seven. But Lord Of Men put up a great show and won by a length from With Fascination. On the same card, Tamure had his first race since his great effort in the Derby, in the Group 3 mile and a quarter Prix du Prince d'Orange. The race developed into a sprint, and the fact that he was able to hold the very talented Spectrum, a mile and a quarter specialist, and on the soft ground that Spectrum prefers, was brilliant. There was still time for more big wins on Mons, for Luca Cumani in the Royal Lodge (Group 2) at Ascot, and on Flemensfirth in the Group 2 Prix Dollar at Longchamp before all the excitement of Lammtarra in the Arc. Lammtarra's absence from the Breeders' Cup and Halling's inability to cope with the dirt track and Cigar at Belmont Park, New York, made that meeting an anti-climax for me and Godolphin. I did have rather better luck on a trip across the Atlantic two weeks before, though, when the great Irish filly Timarida easily won the Group 2 E. P. Taylor Stakes at the Woodbine track in Toronto, Canada. Ten months later, Timarida made another raid on dollars, US this time, and won the Beverley D Stakes at the beautiful Arlington Park track in Chicago.

By the time the season ended in Britain, I had clocked up 217 winners, amazing considering I'd not been so aggressive on the all-weather at the start of the year and my summer injury at Haydock. I'd also ridden abroad a fair bit, admittedly in most cases on Sunday, but to get within sixteen of the score I'd made the year before was something. I understand that Fred Archer, the best jockey of the last century, and Sir Gordon Richards, by far the most dominant personality of the pre-war and immediate post-war era before Lester Piggott took centre stage, were the only others to get 200 wins more than once. I know there are more opportunities now with the all-weather, night meetings, Sunday racing and above all the chance to fly between meetings, but to think that Lester, Pat Eddery and Willie Carson never managed it once, while only Jason and Muis Roberts of the others have done it at all, makes me proud of my achievement.

5 A Typical Season

The knowledge that I had won the jockeys' championship twice in succession gave me a good feeling as I contemplated the winter when my time would be split between riding and a couple of short holiday breaks. The first time I won the title it came as a great relief. The second championship was much different. I really enjoyed it. As I approached the end of the year, everything seemed really set up for a third title. I was sure of one thing: I would be going all out for the hat-trick. And with John Gosden and Godolphin, as well as David Loder, Ian Balding and Luca Cumani backing me up, I had to feel I had a favourite's chance.

I had been attached to John Gosden's stable for two years and we were looking forward to a good time with his three-year-olds which had shown so much promise in their first season. Godolphin, the brainchild of Sheikh Mohammed, was also going to make a major contribution to my season, luck permitting. The Godolphin team consisted of the

Sheikh, his racing manager Simon Crisford, trainer Saeed bin Suroor and his new assistant Tom Albertrani.

For a top jockey, the racing year goes on for all 365 days, however the domestic title race is arranged, and unless you are careful it can sweep you up. At the end of the 1995 season I did manage some time off, but I was pleased to get the chance to ride again in Hong Kong at the big December meeting, where they stage three valuable international races over various distances.

So on 15 December I was back in the colony, two and a half years after I'd had my contract to ride there for a season cancelled. I was due to ride Needle Gun for Clive Brittain and Triarius for Godolphin. I was happy to be there as it gave me a chance to meet up with my good friend Davie Wong, but the day before the races, I received the worst news imaginable.

For some time I had been grateful for the advice and help that Barney Curley, the racehorse trainer, had given me, and I had got to know all his family, especially his young son Charlie, or Chuck, as everyone in Newmarket knew him. Chuck was the sweetest guy in the world, and the news came through from John Gosden that Chuck had been killed in a car crash in Newmarket that morning. It had been a frosty morning and on his way to work he'd skidded on some black ice, had gone into a ditch and been killed outright.

From the time I heard, until the races, it played on my mind and I couldn't have been on the top of my game when Needle Gun ran. Needle Gun was beaten by a neck in his race and, looking back, I'm sure it was partly because I was a bit under the weather.

It was a difficult time. I flew back straight after the races for Chuck's funeral in Newmarket. I'd never been to a funeral before and it was not a comfortable experience for me. All you could do was be there. As I said, I'd been quite close to Barney for a while and it had hit him very very hard.

I was asked to be one of the coffin-bearers from out of the church. The most poignant moment was seeing the effect it had on Chuck's girlfriend. That day was also coincidentally her sixteenth birthday and her grief put everything in perspective for me. She stood there so bravely, so strong. You might lose a race or a ride in a big race and be upset . . . but death is so final, so unforgiving and, in Chuck's case, seemingly such a waste of a good, young life.

It was a very cold, dark midwinter day. I stayed until late afternoon and there were a lot of people there sharing Barney's and his family's grief. One person for whom it was also difficult was Neil Foreman, a pilot who flies a small plane. Most of his work is to do with taking some of the jockeys and trainers to the races up and down the country and he is my regular pilot. Barney often comes along with us if he is interested in going to a meeting in the north of England and he usually takes the mickey out of Neil the whole time. It was after the funeral service at the church that Neil came to Barney's house. I noticed that Barney was looking at Neil quite a lot, but hardly said a word to anyone all day. Then, suddenly, he said to Neil, 'There's no joking now.' He burst into tears and looked so bleak.

I took the night flight back to Hong Kong as I had left Catherine there with Davie Wong and his wife Virginia. I had flown to England, a thirteen-hour flight, straight from the races, went to the funeral and then flew back out again, another thirteen hours, so that by the time I arrived I was exhausted.

Catherine and I stayed in Hong Kong for two days before going away to Phuket to start our holiday. We were there for ten days and had a lovely time, although Christmas in Thailand did not seem quite the same. Still, it was a good rest and we got back on the twenty-eighth, still conscious of the sadness of Chuck's death, but rested and ready for a solid year's work.

Before starting to ride on the all-weather in February, I had organised a two-week skiing holiday for Catherine and me and my best friend Colin Rate and his fiancée Alex. I own a small ski chalet in Mejève in France. The accommodation is very limited – just one bed, a couch and two bunk beds – but we had a great time.

Catherine and Colin had never been skiing before, so I appointed myself as the teacher. The first day I made them go right up to the top of the difficult runs and it took two hours to get down. They walked most of the way and told me I was crazy to take them there. But by the fourth day Colin was getting braver and followed me everywhere. Unfortunately, during the day he fell over and hurt his leg so badly that six months later he was still limping. For the last week while we were there, we had to do our best to keep him entertained. It was a good job we had a Monopoly set.

It is great to take a holiday to recharge the batteries. During the racing season at home, the days are very long, especially when the night meetings come along. You can be on the gallops at six thirty in the morning, ride four or five horses, travel to one race meeting late in the morning, fly on to another, and if the last race is very late, possibly have to drive home the last leg to Newmarket, sometimes not getting home before midnight.

But for me, a holiday is often the start of a worrying time. When we got back from skiing, I was 9st 2lb, 11lb more than my minimum riding weight. Luckily, I had a few weeks before I was due to start to ride on the all-weather, and because the jockeys had decided unanimously to revert to a March to November season to calculate the jockeys' championship in 1996, I was able to pick and choose when, where and how often I would ride, a big change from the two previous years, when I was flat out from 1 January.

So, straight away, I was back on my diet. To be frank, I'd pigged everything in France and enjoyed the food and also the chance to relax and eat the wrong things for once. Some jockeys can eat anything and never have to sweat. For instance, my father had shoulders like a miniature Mike Tyson, had boxed and done weights in his younger days and yet never needed to watch his weight. He is just five feet tall, and I'm taller, without the shoulders, but I have a different metabolism. When I was an apprentice growing up in England, I ate all the wrong food, all the junk food from the various fast-food outlets in town. In that respect, I was no different from most of the stable lads in the town. In the early days, when money was a factor, you just rushed the first thing down you, but as I grew and began to gain weight the question of my diet became not just a factor, but the most compelling factor in my life. At eighteen most people thought I had a weight problem, and I did, but when you think how Ray Cochrane, whose natural weight is nearer 10st than 8st, manages to ride somewhere near that weight, you can see that controlling weight can be achieved.

The question of diet for a jockey is something he can learn to cope with only through experience. Early in my apprenticeship I did not get many rides, and in those days I was totally undedicated. I ate lots of ice-cream, junk food and lots of sweet things. At the same time I hardly ever ate a proper meal. Once I started to get more rides, going to the races and actually being there more with the jockeys helped me start controlling things.

Most jockeys who do have a weight struggle try a few things before settling on the right method, which in all honesty can only be eating sensibly and watching the calories. One thing I tried was using laxatives. At first one or two tablets would have the desired effect, emptying the stomach quite efficiently. But as my body got used to the tablets, I needed to take more and more, so that it took four or five to make things work. That was an unpleasant method, to say the least.

For a while I used to play squash wearing quite a heavy sweatsuit, and another old-fashioned and drastic method was to travel to the races in midsummer wearing warm clothes, keeping the windows shut, with the heater full on. When you got to the track, you felt you'd had half a dozen rides already and it was hardly the ideal preparation for a race.

Many racecourses have a sauna, and most of the top jockeys also have one at home, and if you are, say, a pound and a half too heavy for a ride, spending a little time in the track's sauna usually gets rid of the final necessary ounces.

You soon learn as a jockey that weight is the perennial worry. If you control your weight, you are in control of your life. Sometimes there is a temptation to try to get below your normal minimum for a special fancied ride, but it rarely pays off and often can harm the jockey's health in the short-term, especially in the summer when you are losing a lot of liquid anyway.

The least wise and least successful method I tried, happily for just a couple of weeks, happened when I first went to ride in the United States in the winter of 1990. One day, I was in the jockeys' room when one of the local riders gave me a small tablet about the size of a Tic-tac sweet, rather smaller than a Smartie. It was a Lasix tablet. Lasix is primarily used in racing in America to prevent horses bursting blood vessels. Its use is outlawed in Europe but a majority of States in the US allow it. In fact, most tracks, with their long meetings of up to 365 consecutive days, could not keep the show on the road without Lasix and Bute, which is a painkiller.

The weights are lower for the jockeys in the United States than here and obviously some of the jockeys need to find extra help from somewhere to keep their rides. So, anyway, I took one Lasix tablet and within an hour I'd lost four pounds. But then came the side effects: after one ride my calves cramped up, my eyes felt as though they were in the back of my head. I felt terrible. After I had been taking the Lasix on and off for two weeks, I finally gave up, and I blew up like a balloon.

Over the next couple of years, I continued in the same way, doing well enough and riding plenty of winners for Luca and other trainers who liked to use me on their horses. But, eventually, during a personal crisis, I had to look for more reliable methods of controlling my weight and so, and really for the first time in my professional life, I turned to my dad for advice. He made me realise that for years I had been getting by on my talent, without any dedication to my job. I had been lazy, not thinking about where I was and not happy in myself and what I had achieved. He had been a jockey for thirty-five years and, as I've said, was lucky that he could eat what he wanted and keep a steady weight. If I allowed my weight to stay at its natural level, I'd probably be around 9st 4lb. During the season, however, I have to have a body weight of 8st 3lb to be able to ride at 8st 5lb on my lightest saddle. Dad told me that the key was always to start the season at your lightest so you would be free to think about the rest of the job without having the constant battle with the scales.

Even when a jockey is comfortable and managing his weight well, he always jumps on the scales at home every morning. All the calls to his agent about the forthcoming rides concentrate on whether he is 'doing light' – his minimum – weight, and then the minor sacrifices have to be made.

On a normal day I would have a cup of coffee and maybe a biscuit in the morning. During the summer when the weather is hot, a Diet Coke is not harmful calorie-wise and I like the taste, too. At the races, the tracks all provide sandwiches in the weighing room, and sometimes when you feel hungry, you grab a bite or two. Most people seem to think it's easy keeping your weight down when it's hot, but I find the cold weather better. However tough it gets, though, I insist on eating a meal at night, however late I might get back from an evening meeting. Catherine is a good cook and she's building up a good range of recipes which are not too high in calories. Luckily, I do not really like beef, which is high in fat and therefore calories, so I normally eat either chicken or fish. Catherine has one particular recipe for chicken with salad, where she cuts the chicken meat into small cubes and puts it in with the salad and some fresh Parmesan cheese. I could eat that for dinner – and lunch while I was injured – every day.

The midsummer part of the year provides plenty of exercise to keep the weight down. Riding work early in the morning, maybe up to ten rides at two meetings during the day, is hard work. But when there's a little less of a hectic schedule I sometimes go for a run in the morning, or for a swim at the pool in the Bedford Lodge Hotel in Newmarket.

I mentioned earlier that most days during the height of

the racing season are long and arduous for jockeys, that once you start the treadmill in the spring you cannot really jump off from what has become for many of us a seven-day week until November at the earliest, unless you make a special effort to take time off. Of course, an injury, like the one I had in 1996, or a ban by kind permission of the stewards, another of my 1996 'privileges', will mean you get a less welcome period 'off the treadmill'.

The racing season for the top flat-race jockeys, and even for those lower down the scale, can be divided into three parts and the 'normal' day will vary accordingly. The spring, summer and autumn phases of the season are different as the length of the days and therefore the amount of time available for work in the morning and extra race meetings in the evening alters as the year moves on.

Spring

When I come back to England each year, the important thing is my own fitness. Race riding requires an extra edge and after a layoff, like the one with my broken elbow in the summer of 1996, the first few rides back are tough, just as it's hard for a footballer who has been injured or on a summer's break. It's tough until you get into the swim. That's where I find the all-weather racing helps. I think the ideal starting point is early February. David Loder usually starts to have a few runners on the all-weather tracks, and his strike-rate is very high. So it's nice to know that while it's getting you fit, you can clock up a winner or two. Wherever and whenever they come, winners are always welcome, and when it's for a small owner who has just one horse, and he's pleased you've ridden for him, it gives you an extra buzz. Coming back in February gives me a month before March, which is the starting point for the serious work for the horses with Classic potential. That month also gives you the chance to show the lads who have been stuck here through all the cold weather of December and January that you have some respect for them. At this part of the year, you join them in the mornings riding the horses out from the yard.

First lot is a little later at this time, and it's just as well, for Newmarket in midwinter, when there's nothing to stop the cold winds coming from Siberia other than you, can be pretty bleak. At least the lads see you show your face, and they then get a little respect for you too, seeing you pulling your finger out to get out of bed on a cold morning. That time of year is important. John Gosden takes the opportunity to get me to ride many of the horses, and in a big yard like Stanley House, which can have up to 200 horses in training, that takes a while. I think I'm lucky that, when I sit on a horse, in a few seconds I'm able to tell most things about him. It's a technique you develop when you ride every day. You have an affinity, perhaps it's something some people are born with, or it might be taught along the way. The obvious things I believe I can detect are the horse's temperament, which is most important; the way he looks – Is he alert?; his walk and trot. Some horses you can sit on for two seconds without doing anything and know 'he's a good racehorse'. He might be light on his feet, very sharp and full of himself. Others are merely slobs and feel like they have a refrigerator on each foot.

So, at this time, you ride a different horse each day, and at this stage they are not doing much, just a little canter maybe, building up to more exertion later in the spring. You're very aware of how each horse works, and John, like any top trainer, is anxious for me to see and get acquainted with the horses he thinks are going to do the business for the yard. At this stage I'm making a mental list of between perhaps five or ten horses which will be pulling much of the weight for the entire string in the early part of the season. Then once they are identified, one or two of the dark horses can be expected to come along midway through the season, and not always the obvious ones. When I first get back, I expect to get up around six a.m. and go out from the yard at around seven a.m. The walk to the cantering ground takes a while, and after their exercise you walk back, so first lot may not be over until eight thirty when the lads go in to breakfast. I'll normally have my breakfast with John and his wife Rachel, usually just a cup of coffee and a piece of toast, before going home.

By March the days are getting longer, and gradually a little warmer, and the work is a little more serious, stepping up half a gear. One day it's 28 February and winter, and there's not much happening. But go forward just twenty-four hours to 1 March and all of a sudden it's spring – in racing's clock if not in the weather. There's a big difference: everyone's ears are pricked, maybe the bookmakers will open a book on the Lincoln handicap at the end of the month, and the Warren Hill canter, a four-furlong grass gallop up Warren Hill, opens. Now the grass gallops are open, and even though flat racing on grass is not due to start for another three weeks, the trainers have their own very private race, and they are immediately off and running. It's the 'Who Can Get to the Gallops First Stakes' and however early anyone else starts in the mornings, there's only ever one winner. Clive Brittain has done many amazing things in his career, being one of the few British trainers to win a Breeders' Cup race, as he did with Pebbles, and the first to win the Japan Cup, with Jupiter Island. But Clive is even better at being first string out every morning. There's just no betting: it's like Manchester United being in the Vauxhall Conference. But even for the 'normal stables' the start is earlier. Instead of pulling out at seven a.m. the teams go out half an hour earlier and then another two weeks later it'll be at six.

It might seem a silly race, but, with the number of horses in training there, even the large area of gallops at Newmarket can soon get chewed up with all the horses going over them, especially in a wet spring. So we get a Premier League of teams following Clive out. Godolphin are always early; so is John, and David Loder and Luca Cumani are not far behind. Of the top stables, Henry Cecil is normally last out, but it's simply the trainer's mentality which governs when they go out, and clearly the end results probably do not get affected much.

In my time with Luca Cumani I never had much money and wanted to make a little extra. I had noticed that when we were on our way to work we nearly always used to see Clive's horses on their way back. Rae Guest was one of Luca's jockeys – he is now a very skilful trainer in his own right – and he said I should have a word with Clive if I wanted extra work. So I went to Carlburg Stables and spoke to Clive, who said, 'Yes, sure. We pull out at four thirty.' In those days I had a Vespa moped, which had gears which you had to wrestle with manually. The idea was that I would meet Clive's horses on the Limekilns, one of the main galloping grounds north of the town, but I had to use my moped to get there and leave it where I jumped on the horse I was riding work.

Very few of Clive's lads knew how to ride a moped, or anything else, so, while I was doing the work up the hill on the horse, the lad whose horse I was working had to push this awkward little machine up after me in order to hand the bike over to me again at the top. You can imagine how popular I was with Clive's lads. I managed to keep going to ride out there for three months, by which time I couldn't sleep and was simply exhausted. One thing my exertions did achieve was my first Royal Ascot mount, which was on Clive's filly Merle, on whom I did 7st 6lb in the Royal Hunt Cup. After the three months I told Clive that I'd have to stop coming as Luca's string had started going out a bit earlier and I would not be able to get back in time. I'm sure Clive saw through that excuse.

Like the horses, the jockeys have to get used to the new routine. So I have six weeks to adjust to the earlier starts, while the horses are building up for more important days ahead. In March, first lot will take around one and a half hours. First the horses will walk around a ring for twenty minutes to stretch their legs. Then they will have a little jog or warm up to check whether they are sound. That's the time when the lad riding the horse can tell the trainer if there is a problem, at which point the horse would probably be taken back to his box. The others will go off to the walking grounds, and then have a warm-up canter. Then they will take their turns to work, in the early days working a short distance before walking home again. People wonder why having a horse in training is such an expensive luxury. With an hour and a half out each morning, plus all the grooming and feeding back in the yard, the lad will spend upwards of twenty hours a week with each of his three horses. Even with the modest rates of pay which stable lads receive, and then with the costs of feeding, veterinary and shoeing bills, racehorses are obviously a costly proposition.

As March continues, gradually my riding out days from the yard finish. It is more important as the racing gets ever nearer for the stables to assess the progress of the horses.

Now, on the main work days – Tuesday, Wednesday, Friday and Saturday – there will be fast work and trials to be carried out for various trainers. Most horses ready to race are given fast work once a week and the jockeys go to the gallops by car to meet the horses which they are to partner in the fast workouts. The lad who looks after the horse jumps off and the jockey jumps on. That way he can ride a number of horses on any work morning, getting to know them in good time for when they race. He can also tell the trainer his opinion of how they are progressing. At this time, I spread myself around in order to find some more business. That's when I slot in work for David Loder and Luca Cumani.

The days of each week differ, too. Monday is an easy day for the horses, who usually need to get started again after what for most has been an easy Sunday. The exception, of course, is when they have a race in a few days' time and so also need to have a workout on Sunday. Staff, too, like their weekends off, but the big stables are used to sending runners overseas in the season, and now there's Sunday racing here, too. It's like planning a military operation, running a stable like John's.

For me, Monday is usually my chance to take the morning off to catch up with some sleep. The four work days are invariably busy, with a five forty-five start as the season begins. There's just time for a quick wash and my mandatory cup of coffee before getting to the gallops by six fifteen or, if I'm lucky, six thirty to meet John's first lot. At that time of year, we'll probably be on Racecourse Side, where the gallop runs parallel with the Rowley Mile racecourse. I'll jump up and give a little canter to see that the horse is all right and then, depending on what the trainer wants me to do – that's why he's the trainer – I'll ride according to instructions. All the time I'm building up a store of information about the horses I will be riding in the coming weeks, and hopefully a store of rides on 'outside' horses with chances of winning races. Like Monday, Thursday is a quiet day for most stables and another chance for a little rest.

By the middle of the month, the first Doncaster runners are already in trim for their races and for me, I can't wait to get up in the mornings. Good or bad, every day you find out something new. Before this time, you have learnt seventy per cent about your horses. Now you'll discover another twenty per cent, and while you may be pretty sure of what they can do, it's not until they get to the track and operate under race conditions that the final ten per cent becomes clear. Sometimes there's great news, sometimes disaster, but it's a new year and another chance to get a big horse for the owners, the trainer, the lads and the stable jockey. Everyone has that hope. When you swap over the horses with the lads in the morning they want to see you come back and tell them their horse finished in front in the gallop. Their attitude is so refreshing. Then, once the races start towards the end of the month, it becomes even busier.

You have to carry on with everything else, but when I go back for breakfast with John, that's when I'll be looking through the racing papers to have a glance at the races I'll be riding in. Then I'll go home, and I always try to get an hour in bed before travelling off to the races. It's a kind of routine and seems to help relax me at a time when it's ben-eficial. That's my best sleep of the day and it's not sur-prising I need it, getting up so early. When I wake up, I have a more detailed look at the races for that day, trying to get a clue how each race will be run and what tactics I'll need to get the best out of my rides.

Getting ready for the track, one thing I really enjoy is putting on a tie and a suit. It makes me feel smart and makes me feel good. I think a champion in any sport should behave like a champion and be an example to his colleagues. Depending on whether I need to lose a pound or so, I might have a sauna for half an hour. Other mornings, I could even have the luxury of a lie in, although in the busy part of the spring that doesn't happen too often. When it's time to go, Andy Keates, my driver, will arrive. He's never late and in the six years he's been with me he's never missed a day through illness. As we travel, I'll have another look at the papers and then probably make a few calls to trainers and my agent Matty Cowing before grabbing around twenty minutes' sleep.

Summer

A different tempo and different objectives compared with the spring. By summer, all the early hopes in the major three-year-old races will have been decided one way or the other. It's amazing how quickly we get through the classic trials in the spring and into the two summer classics, the Derby and the Oaks at Epsom, before another short step to Royal Ascot. By now the evening meetings are in full swing, and the schedule gets ever more hectic. Luckily, John appreciates how busy my life is and only needs me to ride out four times a week, and ride work only two mornings, Wednesday and Saturday. The work-day gallops get even earlier and now it's a case of up at five, breakfast at seven till seven thirty, and back home for a proper look at the day's racing, which is now always a double-header except on Tuesdays, more calls to Matty and any trainers I need to speak to, and then the customary hour in bed.

The motorways of Britain have finished off more jockeys than anything else. Jockeys like George Duffield and his younger counterpart Jimmy Quinn have travelled many thousands of miles in the quest for a winner. Pat Eddery, Willie Carson and Walter Swinburn all realised that the use of a plane, despite the cost, is a great help in staving off the exhaustion which can hit a jockey at any time. In the summer, the roads are crowded with traffic, and Fridays spent travelling north up the M6 are a recipe for madness. I met Neil Foreman a few years ago, when he was flying Michael Roberts during the season when he won more than 200 races and won the title. I had a chat with Neil and said that I would be going for the title myself and expected to be a lot busier, and asked whether he would fly me around. Now I fly as often as I can and the benefit, apart from getting to the track much more quickly, is the extra time I get to relax at home in the mornings. There's no question that since I've been going to the races by plane, I last the year out longer. Instead of six hours a day in a car, I take just a fraction of that time if I fly. It doesn't come cheap, though. Jockeys are expected to pay all their own expenses out of their riding fees and prize money percentage, and on average it costs £150 a day to fly. Over three months that's a lot of money, but we usually share, and jockeys like Willie Ryan and Jimmy Quinn, who've got fed up with the motorways like me, are regulars, as, for some of the big meetings, are Barney Curley and David Loder. We're all founder members of the unofficial Newmarket Flyers' Club. We have a verbal agreement. Neil needed the business and I needed the plane. It's a great arrangement for both of us. And because I get to ride in most of the races at the meetings I attend, I rarely have to wait for anyone else to finish before flying off. They have to wait for me!

To pay for the massive expenses, my agent Matty Cowing has to work even harder than would otherwise be the case. When he books a ride he checks with Neil whether I would need to leave an afternoon meeting, say, a race earlier to make the first ride at the evening meeting. That creates lots of problems for Matty and Neil to sort out. There are only a few tracks where you can land on the middle of the course. Newmarket, Newbury and Haydock all allow planes to land; Newmarket has a strip at the end of the July course and the other two have a strip in the middle of the track. In other instances, taxis have to be laid on from the nearest airfield, which, almost invariably, is a grass strip, often in some pretty out-of-the-way place. All those arrangements are made by Neil, a former policeman in the CID in Hackney, East London, and therefore capable of looking after himself.

For a jockey to take the mount in a race he needs to be fully dressed in his colours, and on the scale with his saddle at least fifteen minutes before the advertised time of the race, and if he's not there in time – fourteen minutes forty-five seconds is just too late – there will be a queue of his colleagues ready to take the bread out of his mouth. Usually, a couple of times a year you are held up going for what turns out to be a winning ride and when you arrive someone will be there warming up the colours for you. If the stewards decide you have not allowed enough time, they will fine you, but as long as Matty and Neil do their job, that doesn't happen and the stewards are understanding.

If Neil is important to me in the summer, Matty is my right hand all year round. He is one of the members of Newmarket's most exclusive club, Ladbrokes betting shop regulars society, of which Dave Shippy Ellis, who is agent for Gary Carter among others, and Blue Duster's famous lad, Billy, who is a great expert on the dog racing from Walthamstow, are also valued members. When I was fifteen, I spent every afternoon in the betting shop, and got to know Matty. He has been my agent ever since and helps enormously.

People outside racing think a jockey leads a glamorous life, where champagne and caviar are the staple foods. But it is only the top three or four who get a good living, and for the past few years I have been lucky to get into that group. For most of the middle-rank riders, however, the expenses are killing. To be able to get to the track, they have to run a reliable car. That is expensive in relation to their income, and then, what with running it, and the cost of petrol and the infinitely higher costs of servicing a car that does 80,000 miles a year, they live from hand to mouth in most cases. The car's value soon drops and as your life gets so intense you have to pay someone to drive you to the track or you would be falling asleep at the wheel. Suppose a jockey gets one booked ride at Edinburgh. He has to drive all the way from Newmarket and spend £200 getting there and all he gets if the horse is unplaced is his £61 riding fee. He's out of pocket by £140. When I fly to the races, I have to think of my first three or four rides, if they are out of the money, as just paying the expenses before I start earning, and that's someone who is doing okay. The less fortunate jockeys have to cut corners and costs, sharing lifts when possible. That's why I never mind giving a lift to a young jockey if there's room.

Racing here is definitely underfunded. At a lot of meetings there's not even a prize for fourth. It's hard on the owners, the trainers who depend on their share of the prize money to make up what a lot of them lose through subsidising training fees, and on the jockeys, too. If there was a fourth prize, even just £300, the paltry extra £20 the jockey would earn would at least go a little way towards helping him meet his costs. It would also help form in the less valuable races to be more reliable. If there were worthwhile fourth places available, all the jockeys would ride out properly for fourth instead of not bothering. As things are now, if a jockey does ride out properly for fourth where there is no prize money for that placing, the owner and trainer are more likely to be furious with him, saying that if he had allowed the horse to coast the last 100 yards, he would have got a better handicap mark the next time.

Some days are made even more tiring for me because the time of my last ride at the evening meeting means that we cannot reach the Newmarket strip before dark. Neil is a good pilot and daring enough to trust his skill on what is a beautifully maintained strip, but the regulations do not allow him or us to risk it. So, even if we fly to the night meeting, Andy will often have to drive there himself to get me back home. On those occasions we will often have extra passengers, but I try to remember to remind myself of all the lifts I got when I needed them when I was a struggling apprentice.

Whatever my day, good or bad, I always like to eat a meal, however late it is. Most times, my lovely fiancée Catherine will have made me a salad and left it ready for me. I'll have had a packet of crisps and a Diet Coke in the car coming home, and then I'll take half an hour to get over the day before eating. Then, five minutes later, it's bed and back on the treadmill again in the morning, a procedure we follow for three months, when we're constantly living on adrenalin.

Autumn

By the time of the York Ebor meeting in August, and from then until the St Leger meeting at Doncaster in early September, most of the jockeys who have had a clear run will be going around like zombies. In 1996, my various absences through suspension and then injury meant that I was fresh while everyone else wanted a break, but normally we are all in the same boat. At this time, all of a sudden, the evening meetings finish and we're back to a similar schedule to the spring with one meeting a day and a maximum of five or six rides. You revert to a more normal life, and the past exertions catch up on you. For the whole of that fortnight most jockeys spend almost every spare minute catching up on the sleep they have gone without for so long. Your body, whose complaints you have been ignoring for the whole of the past three months, finally gets the message through that you need to sleep, and now you can finally listen.

York and Doncaster are two meetings I always enjoy. Both tracks are great to ride, Doncaster a true test of stamina, while the Ebor meeting, on the beautiful, manicured York track, features so many good races and top-class horses. By now the activity at home is settling down again, till it's almost as it was in the spring, although the emphasis now, instead of being on the Classic generation of three-year-olds, is on next year's stars. The dream in all the stables at this time is that those young horses, so carefully broken in the year before, and gently brought along all summer, will show something to say they will be the following year's stars. You might have a major candidate for the St Leger, Arc or Champion Stakes in September and October. Their training will be carefully monitored. Meanwhile the better-class two-year-olds are being lined up, either for the important back-end juvenile races, or for one of the maiden events on the major tracks, which are normally won by horses with a big future.

By now, with the days closing in, the top jockeys are also lining things up. Either a new job for a big stable for the following year, or a winter contract, preferably in one of the overseas countries, such as Hong Kong or Japan, where the pay can be very rewarding. Keeping busy then can put the whole year's work on a sound commercial basis. For me, I love the thought and anticipation of travelling round the world. As the days get colder in England, the idea of warm weather is very tempting. By October, you are invariably tired, having worked your butt off all year.

The attractions and warmth of some of the world's beauty spots in winter cannot alter the appeal of New-market. Although Italian, I think now of Newmarket as my home. My fiancée is from there and my work and home are there. Of course, when the east winds blow, Newmarket can be pretty bleak, but I find it more beautiful in winter than in summer. Of course, the trees have no leaves, but on most mornings the trees and grass are covered with frost which gives a dreamy atmosphere. On a lovely clear morning I enjoy seeing the horses (and the lads, if they are sensible) wrapped up warmly against the cold, and to see the breath from their nostrils turn to steam as it meets the cold air. Italy is reckoned to be warmer than England, but winters are just as cold in my original home town, Milan, as they are here in England. Nowadays, there's plenty of good thermal equipment. In winter I wear skiing thermals, top and bottom, made of silk. Above them, I have a thick pair of jodhpurs and then a top layer of a thick pair of riding-out waterproofs. The only inconvenience with looking like the Michelin Man is that all the clothing restricts freedom of movement, but at that time of year you don't have to do anything too serious on a horse. I don't think you ever really get used to the cold, and one area for which I haven't really found an effective remedy is in the hand department. You can't really ride out in boxing gloves, after all. If someone could find a light glove which could keep you warm in the cold weather I'd pay him a big bonus.

I'm very pleased to live in Newmarket. I find it nice to escape into the freedom of the countryside, which you find all around the town. In London, the life is enjoyable, but the place is too mean and for me and there would never be any escape. How can you say Hyde Park would be an escape? It's nice to have the freedom which the Newmarket area gives you.

As a training centre, Newmarket is as good as anywhere in the world. The variety of the gallops and their quality is the best in the world, and enables the trainers to do an excellent job. The popularity of Newmarket means that sometimes there can be a little congestion when hundreds of horses are preparing to go up a particular gallop at the same time. The one improvement I would like to see would be the addition of an American-style oval dirt track.

6 The Start of the 1996 Season

The start of the 1996 season brought about a welcome change for me and all the jockeys who felt that riding twelve months a year was unwise. Before the advent of all-weather racing, the flat in Britain began at Doncaster at the end of March and ended back at Doncaster in early November. That had been the format for many years. All-weather racing began not because anyone felt a need to prolong the flat-race season. Originally, it was brought in to compensate for the lost jumping fixtures in the worst of the winter, which, in practice, is usually January and February. So while Lingfield's first meeting on their new all-weather track was on the flat, the main reason behind it had been to provide a more reliable surface in cold weather on which to stage jump races while the turf tracks might be frozen or covered with snow. It soon became obvious that the artificial surfaces at Lingfield and Southwell, the other all-weather track, were not ideal for jumping, and the number of

93

injuries to horses led to a campaign against all-weather jumping after a couple of seasons.

Racing in Britain is funded through a levy on betting and, with the failure of all-weather jumping, the authorities quickly introduced more and more all-weather flat racing to make up for it. So the original idea, to give alternative chances for jump owners, trainers and jockeys, was lost. Perhaps that's why they now have a programme of summer jumping.

People think we flat jockeys are over-paid but whatever they pay the jump boys cannot be enough, and they do, I admit, earn less than us, what with time out through falls. If a flat jockey is unlucky, like I was with Shawanni at Newbury, he can have an unexpected fall and be out for weeks, or even months as in my case. But those guys: when they go out they know that every so often they'll be falling, probably at a great big fence. I rode in only one hurdle race, an invitation event at Chepstow between the flat and jump jockeys, and I was absolutely terrified. They must be mad. No wonder Ray Cochrane and John Williams concentrated on getting their weight right and going back on the flat. Even Lester used to ride jumping winners before he learnt to live on a cigar and a glass of champagne forty years or more ago. The bravery and skill of people like Richard Dunwoody and Peter Scudamore amazes me. Okay, they don't have to worry about the kind of skin burns they used to get when falling on an all-weather track. Now they can bump their heads on the hard summer turf instead.

But to return to us pampered flat-racing boys. Whereas Jason Weaver and me had both gone flat out on the sand tracks, to which has now been added Wolverhampton and its trend-setting floodlights, Pat Eddery, Willie Carson, John Reid, Walter Swinburn and Richard Quinn had all stayed away, perhaps with the exception of the odd ride when it suited John and Richard. There had been a feeling for a couple of years that something had to be done, that it was an artificial situation when someone, as I had a couple of years before, got fifty-one winners on the board before Pat had started polishing his riding boots in time for Doncaster.

Even Jason and me were aware something needed to be done. In a year we were clocking up not just 1,000 rides, but 200,000 miles in planes, cars and helicopters in a season which went unbroken from 1 January until November. In both our cases, that could not have been possible without the great help of our agents. Jason is looked after by the journalist Terry Norman, but my agent, Matty Cowing, is one of the celebrities of Newmarket. He started as agent to Bruce Raymond and took me on after refusing to sign me up for some time. Every day we will talk by telephone, in the mornings after first lot, and then, through the day, as he compiles my list of rides for the coming days. As I have become more successful, his skill has become more important, as he sifts the best chance from those mounts offered by trainers and owners hoping to get me on their horses. In the weighing room after a race you will often hear a jockey picking up his mobile phone and calling his agent to ask why he wasn't on a certain winner which he considers should have been his ride. It is rare that I reckon Matty has made that kind of mistake, and when he does, there's usually a good reason for accepting another ride instead.

I'm lucky in several ways with Matty. He's been doing the job of an agent for quite a few years now. As a 'face' in Newmarket he already knew a lot of the trainers when he took me on as an apprentice. He works for me and me alone, and that way – and I'm fortunate in that respect – I only have to compete with other jockeys and different agents for rides. I don't think it can be so easy to stop jealousies arising when an agent gets a ride for one of his jockeys that another of his guys thinks should be his. Matty watches almost every race each day in the local Ladbrokes in Newmarket. He gets to know from trainers and also work riders which horses are in form. All of that knowledge, plus many hours' working over the form book, gives him, and therefore me, an edge in what is an increasingly competitive business. Matty knows the form backwards, upside-down and inside-out. His spade work and my own input, either about horses I've ridden or seen in races I've ridden in, plus horses I've ridden on the gallops or heard about, adds to the overall picture. We're a team, just as John and me or Godolphin and me are a team. My first loyalty has to be to either John or Godolphin and when one or the other has a runner in a race at a track I'm going to then there's no question of my taking an outside ride. When they are not involved, then David Loder, Ian Balding or Luca Cumani are the next in line. It's great to have so many good stables on your side wanting to use you. Matty manages to keep them all pretty happy for much of the time, but sometimes of course the clashes are impossible to avoid. Matty's like a favourite uncle, good-natured and great fun. He likes nothing better than backing a winner – except backing a winner I've ridden. Then he gets paid twice – by Weatherbys and Ladbrokes!

When you are involved in racing every day, in some cases from morning till night, the question of studying form is really like the situation in any full-time job. Form means all the races that are run every day. Of course, when you ride for the major stables on the top tracks, you won't be too bothered about the selling races on minor tracks in the north. With more than 4,000 flat races being run every year, you need to be selective. An average field through the season is around ten runners, so multiplying that by 4,000, form involves a total of around 40,000 performances. Just by riding in the 1,000 races I have in my busiest season, I will be aware first-hand of a quarter of everything, and in my case the most significant quarter. In his betting shop, Matty will see a lot of the stuff I miss, but if I'm at home the Racing Channel, which started recently, also helps keep me informed. Jockeys are much less likely to worry about pounds and lengths when assessing the horses in a race. I think it's more important to take the overall picture of a horse – Is he keen? Will he battle? Must he lead? If so, will he be taken on by other front-runners? And so on. From on a horse's back, if you keep your mind clear, you can pick up a lot about the horses others are riding. Just as in a job, it's a matter of experience, and you learn something new every day, if only the fact that, however much you think you know, there is never a real certainty until it crosses the line!

As far as the jockeys are concerned, it is a relief that racing's authorities have not yet organised much all-weather in November and December – but a couple of very cold early winters may even get them looking in that direction. The year before we decided to alter the championship, all the boys in the weighing room were asked when they wanted to run from, but on that occasion nothing was changed. This time there was a free vote and there was a majority of four to one in favour of going back to the old-style championship, based on wins between the start of turf racing at Doncaster and the final day, which for some strange reason now goes on until Folkestone on the Monday after the Doncaster November Handicap, which surely is a much more satisfactory and significant cut-off point.

Riding on the all-weather tracks is very different to riding on grass. I think of it as being a bit like speedway racing. First you must try to make a good break from the gate, and, then, during the race, try to get a smooth run on your horse. That's the most important thing. The reason is that, unlike on turf, when a horse can often quicken in a few strides, on the all-weather it usually takes a horse a furlong to build up to full speed. It's because the top part of the sand is loose to a depth of about three inches and underneath there's much harder sand. So, when galloping, the horse doesn't get such a good grip as he does with turf. Therefore, if a jockey fails to maintain a smooth run and gets checked, he will lose momentum, take that furlong to get going again, by which time the race will be over, for him anyway. When you watch races on dirt in America, or on all-weather here, you immediately are struck by the difference. They race up to five or six wide, all looking for that smooth run, and also to avoid the kick-back which is unpleasant for horses and jockeys. There's nothing worse than swallowing a mouthful of sand while you're trying to ride a race. There's much less weaving around between horses, and, rather than trying to be tactical, all the jockeys are concentrating on not getting stopped in their runs. They don't interfere with anyone else; they are simply doing the best for their own horse. It is very unusual, too, in a dirt race in England or the United States, for a horse which has made the early running, only to be passed in mid-race and drop back, ever to rally and win, unlike on turf where this is much more common. Because the element of luck in running is less of a factor, American horses on the dirt can compile longer winning sequences than the turf horses. It's true Cigar is a star performer and had to be tough and talented to set a sequence of sixteen wins in a row, but the task would have been much harder to achieve on turf. Here, racing is so competitive, it's rare for a horse to win even six times in a row. He needs to be a star to do that, whereas even in the short time of all-weather racing we've had several horses winning many times. In my view, the dirt specialist will win on dirt, and the grass horse of a similar quality will win the argument on turf, just like a Wimbledon champion on the grass courts would have trouble on the different artificial surfaces in Paris, Australia and New York. The Triple Crown in British racing is as elusive as the Grand Slam in men's tennis and the clean sweep of golf's four majors.

The all-weather will no doubt continue to expand and it's great for some of the less fashionable jockeys that their skills can be appreciated. The all-weather season in 1996 proved a great boost for Ray Cochrane, as it had been for me in the two previous years, and both he and Gay Kelleway, who is showing so much promise as a trainer, took advantage of the opportunities. Another jockey who works hard, probably harder than anyone, is Jimmy Quinn. Jimmy is a latter-day George Duffield, going thousands of miles up and down the motorways in search of rides and winners. He's a regular on the sand tracks and I'm delighted that he's getting chances to ride good horses, like Merit, on whom he won the Chester Cup.

When people talk about jockeys and the amount of riding they do, the temptation to compare Britain with America or France is hard to avoid. American jockeys ride many more races than we do, but the top jockeys, apart from flying from one side of America to the other for a special ride in a big race, will stay in their own location. Chris McCarron is based in California. He'll rotate between Hollywood Park and Santa Anita, both in the Los Angeles area, for the whole year, with a break in August when he will be in Del Mar, the track in Southern California right by the ocean, which is

California's answer to Deauville in France, or Saratoga, for the New York riders. We have the odd day at Yarmouth or Brighton, so why should we complain?

The American meetings at some tracks continue for the entire year. The seasons at Santa Anita, the principal Californian track, and Hollywood last for a couple of months or more, and for the jockeys it gets to be rather like going to the office. They ride track work in the mornings, go home for a rest, and then it's back to the track for the afternoon. So they might ride in up to ten or eleven races every day, but they have none of the travel wear and tear that we have here.

The French tracks for the top jockeys are all in the Paris region, although with the imminent closure of Evry, a really nice track on the outskirts of Paris, they will be making more use of tracks like Lyon-Parilly. In August, they all move down to Normandy for a very pleasant month at Deauville, when the locals are likely to bump into Cash Asmussen, Thierry Jarnet or Olivier Peslier in one of the many popular racing cafés in the seaside town.

Here, though, it could be Pontefract on Monday, Bath on Tuesday, Sandown on Wednesday, a day at Yarmouth and then a couple of afternoons at Haydock. Sometimes, with all the travelling, you might just start to think how lucky those Americans are knowing that they will be based in the same place for months at a time, apart from the occasional flight for one of the big races out of town. However, because, as far as my riding education is concerned, I have been brought up in England, I believe that if I were to ride regularly in the United States for any length of time, I'd soon find it boring. It would probably become a question of doing the same thing every day, like going to work at the office: saying 'Goodbye, darling' to my fiancée, as I leave in the morning, and staying shut away in the jockeys' room under the stands every afternoon. The same environment, the same people, and on the ordinary days when even the good American tracks offer ordinary races, the same horses, too.

Here, it's much different. All through the season we have big meetings to look forward to on different tracks, which all pose their own particular problems to the riders. There's the Guineas meeting at Newmarket, Epsom for the Derby and Oaks; Royal Ascot; Goodwood; York; and the St Leger at Doncaster. For good measure, some of us are lucky enough to make regular trips over to France and Ireland for the major races there. Even with all the travelling, the variety makes life tolerable. There's a light at the end of the darkest tunnel – if you are lucky, that is.

The tracks offer variety and a number of different challenges. The hardest to ride is Longchamp. It takes a long time to master France's premier racecourse, with its false straight which is really still some way from the finishing part of the action. In some ways, I think I've rewritten the way to ride the track, where for so long the only correct way of riding there was to follow the pattern of the great French jockey Yves Saint-Martin. He, of course, was the French counterpart and international rival of Lester Piggott for many years and his style at Longchamp reflected the way the French train their horses. In England, the emphasis in training is on stamina and the races are accordingly run at a decent pace. In France, speed and more speed is the emphasis and the races have traditionally been run at a much steadier pace, with all the jockeys coming with a flying late run. I have found that if you take an English horse to run in France and try to play the French jockeys' way, they will swamp you for speed in the last furlong. So to counter this you have to be really bold. I learnt over three or four years that if you go there with even half a query in your mind, you'll get beaten. Boldness pays, and I always try to make sure I ride that way when I go there for any race, but especially a big one.

When I got back to England after my skiing holiday in February 1996, I had arranged to ride a few horses, mainly for David Loder and Reg Hollinshead, on the all-weather tracks. The winners – and I rode nine – might not count for the championship any more, but the riding helped get me back into shape and ready for my first big challenge of 1996, far away in the Arabian desert.

The rise in importance of Arab owners over the past twenty years in racing has been steady and spectacular. The Maktoum family from Dubai, one of the emirates which form the United Arab Emirates, has become easily the most important owning group in the world, and their love of horses is not just a modern development. The breed of the thoroughbred developed from the importation almost 300 years ago of a number of stallions from Arabia. Three of them, the Byerley Turk, the Godolphin Barb or Arabian, and the Darley Arabian are the forerunners of all the present representatives of the breed nowadays known as 'thorough-bred'. It is significant that the family, and Sheikh Mohammed in particular, who is Crown Prince in Dubai, should use the names Darley and, more recently, Godolphin for the two distinct portions of his wide bloodstock interests.

Darley Stud Management is the name under which Sheikh Mohammed's horses, which run in his name and in that of his younger brother Sheikh Ahmed, and horses owned by friends and relatives such as Saeed Manana, are managed from Newmarket. Darley Stud controls up to

1,000 horses in training, and Anthony Stroud is its racing manager. The smaller Godolphin Management is run by Simon Crisford, a former racing journalist who first worked for Sheikh Mohammed as Anthony Stroud's assistant. He spends half the year in Dubai, the rest in Newmarket, where the horses managed by Godolphin are trained under the banner of Saeed bin Suroor. In the last few years, Sheikh Mohammed has concentrated much of his energy on developing a fine racecourse in Dubai, and the fruition of his grand design (after a couple of years, when an international jockeys' series was staged) was the 1996 Dubai World Cup.

As stable jockey for John Gosden and for Godolphin, which in both cases meant riding mainly for Sheikh Mohammed, the enormous project of the Dubai World Cup meant a lot to me, as it did to everyone connected with the Maktoum family. Their involvement in British racing has been immense and I have been very lucky to ride some of the best horses to be trained here in recent years. Lammtarra, Balanchine, Moonshell and Halling will always be high up on my list of the best horses I have ridden however long I am a jockey, and I have to thank John for giving me the chance to prove myself, and the Boss, as everyone in Dubai calls Sheikh Mohammed, for the opportunity to ride for Godolphin.

Any race, whether it has astronomical prize money or not, needs a special kick to get it established, and the Dubai World Cup, even allowing for the fact that there was $4 million on offer, needed to attract a true star to give it credibility. I remember what the critics and cynics said when news of the Dubai World Cup was first released in England: A race in Dubai in late spring on a sand track? It'll only benefit the Maktoum horses who've been preparing in the desert from the autumn. They'll have all the advantages. The English and the Americans might as well not bother – they'll just be there to make the Dubai horses look good.

Sheikh Mohammed, while hoping that the horses originally selected from his and his brothers' strings with such care and trained close to his home in Dubai by Saeed bin Suroor would make a good showing, was more intent on attracting world-class opposition. When owner Allen Paulson agreed to bring Cigar to Dubai, the future of the race was pretty secure. Mr Paulson had been the original owner of Arazi, the flying machine who'd won the Breeders' Cup and in whom Sheikh Mohammed had bought a half-share. Since then the two men had become well acquainted and Mr Paulson's willingness to put his horse's reputation on the line in a race so far away was commendable. Everyone thought the Dubai horses would have an advantage.

I have to say that Sheikh Mohammed did everything possible to get the organisation of the big day right and the whole thing went like clockwork. I was hopeful of going close. After all, Halling, the horse I eventually chose to ride, had won races on the dirt in Dubai the previous winter and had looked a top-class horse when he'd won the Eclipse Stakes and the International at York the previous summer. True, he'd been nowhere when Cigar had won the Breeders' Cup Classic in New York in 1995 but there'd obviously been something wrong with him then. When he won his warm-up race in Dubai a couple of weeks before the World Cup, we were ready.

As it turned out, if we had all looked at things a little more realistically, the true situation might have occurred to us. Halling and the other Dubai horses had, like Pentire who had come over from England, been reared and trained to race on English turf. The fact that Halling had already done well in Dubai was irrelevant. He had been beating other turf horses on sand. Cigar and the other two American horses showed that a specialist is needed. Cigar had been hopeless on turf and had not begun his record-breaking run until they'd switched him back to dirt tracks. While hoping for a good run from Halling, we had to admit that, in our opinion, Cigar was nearly unbeatable. He won the Dubai World Cup, showing the kind of guts that only a top-class performer can pull out when it's most needed. The Americans were 1–2–3 and the World Cup was a success, as all the many visitors, especially the Americans, many of them there for the first time, agreed. Pentire, in fourth, was giving a nice compliment to his old rival Lammtarra.

The timing of the World Cup, just a few days after the start of the turf season, and then the fact that there is very little good racing in England until the Craven meeting at Newmarket, meant that Doncaster became a little episode of its own. When we go back to Doncaster each year, it's always nice to see all the faces, which in many cases you haven't seen much of since the previous autumn. We all use the three days at Doncaster to catch up on all the news from the winter: where everyone has been riding or on holiday, how they like their new jobs and that sort of thing. The jockeys are basically one big family. They spend more time in each other's company in the weighing room during the year than they do at home. Between the races, until we get changed when we've finished, we just sit and talk together, or watch races from the other meetings. But in March 1996, there was one big difference for me: Walter Swinburn's peg was empty. I usually sit next to Wally, but he had had a terrible fall from an unraced horse in Hong Kong during the winter and had suffered major injuries, of which the worst was to his head. For a while he was on the critical list in intensive care in one of Hong Kong's best hospitals. Happily, he made a complete recovery and the public were able to appreciate his skills again in the summer. In my opinion, Wally has more natural talent than any jockey riding today.

The atmosphere in the jockeys' room can be manic at times, with everyone rushing here and there, but it might surprise people to know that very few of us have nicknames, at least not ones which people are prepared to say to your face. Walter is known, largely because of some pressmen, as The Choirboy, but to us he's simply Wally. One unkind name for a jockey I daren't mention is By-pass, because of the number of times he's been overlooked for a top job. There was a lot more humour in the weighing room when Richard Fox was still riding. Foxy was funny, however well or badly he was doing. Nowadays, though, most of the boys are busy speaking to their agents between rides.

Whereas the jump jockeys go out on the track knowing they will have some falls and can therefore sometimes take action to minimise the consequences, falls on the flat tend to be unexpected. Watching Lester Piggott on two occasions when he did fall from horses revealed just what a great horseman he was. In the Breeders' Cup, the year after his brilliant win on Royal Academy in the first few days of his comeback, Lester came down off the sprinter Mr Brooks. The horse lost his footing, his legs went from under him, but I remember seeing Lester still perfectly balanced as the horse went down. Then, another time, at Goodwood, riding a two-year-old of Richard Hannon's, the saddle came right off, but Lester, cool as ever, stayed on until the last minute, and when he fell he still managed to curl up like a jump jockey before he hit the ground. His injuries, bad enough for a man then already well into his fifties, were nothing compared to what he would have suffered without the knowledge, gained over almost half a century in the saddle, of what to do.

Apart from my latest bad fall in the paddock at Newbury, my worst and most dramatic fall had come at Haydock the previous year. The horse in question was a great favourite of mine. Wainwright was the stable pet at John Gosden's. A tough six-year-old, he was a fine big horse, but had terrible feet and John and his staff did a great job ever getting him on to the track. Anyway, he went to Haydock in August for a Group 3, a race which would probably be his last appearance on the track. It was hoped that if he won or went very close, there might be a job for him somewhere overseas as a stallion, but otherwise there was talk that maybe he could be sold to me so I could give him to Catherine as a riding horse.

The race went well at first, but suddenly, after we turned into the straight, I remember hearing a bang and seeing the ground. Then I can just remember a few flashes, and me being in an ambulance. I felt a terrible pain in my back. Then in hospital afterwards, I kept waking up for a few minutes, but then drifting away again. Before the fall the thought of not being champion would have been as bad as not being able to live. Now, I thought, 'Jesus, what does being champion matter?' At that point it didn't mean anything to me. Here I was in bed with a drip, with a terrible headache and a painful back. I was given two tablets, elephant-sized, probably morphine or something, and I felt as right as rain. After three or four days my head was okay and soon my back was fine, too. It's amazing to think you can fall at that speed and come out of it all right. I've had maybe seven or eight falls like that. Obviously, at first it is a knock to your confidence. For the first two to three weeks you have to worry whether you will feel the same about riding. Some jockeys never truly recover from a bad fall, but in most cases time is a great healer.

Richard Hills and I flew out to Dubai straight after the Kempton bank holiday meeting to ride some of the Godolphin hopefuls. Almost as soon as we arrived, after just a couple of hours' sleep, we were out at the Al Quoz stables, riding horse after horse in fact-finding gallops. By the time we'd finished we were dripping with sweat as, even though it was still very early in the morning, the day was warming up quickly. As I said when describing the Dubai World Cup, not all the horses at Sheikh Mohammed's stables, which are situated just behind the office he uses in his palace, are suited to the sand track. But I was interested to see Mark Of Esteem, who looked in tremendous condition, his coat, like those of many of the other horses there, gleaming with health, and quite a contrast to the majority of horses I'd seen struggling with the continuing cold weather at Newmarket. Another horse which looked in great shape was Mick's Love, which had been bought out of Mark Johnston's stable the previous autumn.

We returned to England for the Craven meeting. The gap between the Doncaster March meeting and the Craven meeting in April seems abnormally long. Even with the Dubai World Cup and the Grand National which follows it, the racegoers in England do not have much to interest them. The fixtures look very unappetising until you get to the Craven meeting and the re-opening of Newmarket. In 1996, in England, the winter went on and on, and by the time the Craven meeting came round, we were wondering if the weather would ever get any better.

For me, the Craven meeting is the most nerve-racking

of the entire year. For everyone in the top stables, all the hopes and expectations of the previous six months are about to be tested. It is hard to over-emphasise just how crucial this time of the year is. The first four of the five English Classics are settled within just over five weeks from the beginning of May to the end of the first week in June, with only the St Leger, far off in September, to come. Yet really the season doesn't get going until the Craven meeting and that is barely two weeks before the two Guineas races.

The trainers all hope their horses will be ready to go well in their trial races and then graduate to the Guineas, or in the case of the more staying types, the Derby and the Oaks. The spring of 1996 was a frustrating one for John Gosden's stable, which, with the Godolphin horses still in Dubai, was taking most of my attention at this stage.

At the end of 1995, John and I believed there were several horses with real Classic chances, especially Lord Of Men, who had won his last three races as a two-year-old, culminating with a fine performance in the Group 1 Prix de la Salamandre. Then, coming into Craven week, we had Pommard, who had won his only race as a two-year-old, Sacho, Santillana and the unraced Shantou backing him up.

By the end of Craven week, Pommard had been well beaten in the Craven Stakes and had fallen out of contention for the Classics; Sacho had been narrowly beaten in his maiden race at Newmarket and was found to have suffered a training problem; and, worst of all, Lord Of Men had sustained quite a serious injury which meant he would be out until autumn at the earliest.

If it is bad for the owner, trainer and jockey, I often wonder how earth-shattering defeat for a Classic hope is for the horse's lad. The trainer will see each horse for a few minutes each day, monitor the horse's work with his lad and then take special notice of the horse on the days he goes to the races. The lad, on the other hand, lives with the horse for as long as the horse is in the stable. Arriving early in the morning, he will muck him out, groom and feed him; he'll encourage him on the gallops and report on his progress each day to the trainer. All his hopes for a good year depend on the horses (usually no more than three) that he looks after. He becomes each horse's nurse, teacher, psychiatrist and biggest defender when other people criticise the horse's ability or honesty. At the start of the year, many of the well-bred horses in the major stables will have their lads dreaming of Epsom and June, and leading in the Derby winner. Sadly, for so many modestly paid, dedicated people, it can only become reality for one.

When Sacho was beaten in the maiden race at New-market, I spent two hours that night walking up and down in my kitchen. I could not believe it. We'd already had to accept that Lord Of Men was going to miss the bulk of the season. Now Sacho. I'd been very pleased with his work and was shocked that he could lose, albeit in the best, maiden company. Pommard had probably been a little too inexperienced to cope with the best of last year's two-year-olds in the Craven Stakes, but events in the next couple of months showed that Beauchamp King, Alhaarth and Rio Duvida, three of the other four runners, were all less impressive as three-year-olds, and only Polaris Flight, who was a place ahead of Pommard in the Craven Stakes and later second in the French and Irish Derbys, had really trained on.

The disappointment with John's horses made this a most unhappy week for me, added to which Ian Balding and David Loder, the other two big stables for which I regularly ride, were also not yet in great form. I felt particularly sorry for David who had been so hopeful that Blue Duster would continue with her unbeaten form which had made her the champion two-year-old filly of 1995. She had a problem and was sent to Dubai in early summer to take advantage of the fine medical facilities which Sheikh Mohammed has developed there.

All the time, I had the feeling that the very cold weather, which went on right until the end of May, was one of the main reasons for the problems in many stables. Horses were simply not thriving as they normally do in a warm spring. Those stables which did hit form early tended to keep it. Those that were out of luck simply had to wait for things to improve.

Usually, though, when you are at your lowest, thinking nothing will happen for you, one horse comes through to save the day. At Stanley House stables, John's head lad Rodney is one of life's great optimists. Every horse he rides is somewhere between Nijinsky and Pegasus, the flying horse, but after a number of times hearing him say to me, 'Have a sit on Santillana, he's a good horse', I finally took him up on it. Santillana had won a little race at Edinburgh, now known as Musselburgh, at the November meeting, hardly the time or the place to look for Classic clues, but when I sat on him I had to agree he was a nice type.

I was in Dubai when Santillana made his three-year-old début in a small race at Ripon. He won it with a little to spare and, even though he didn't have the Derby engagement, John let him take his chance in the Sandown Classic Trial. Although on his ratings he was miles behind the others on form, several of John's lads were more than hopeful. I have to admit I was surprised when he beat Glory Of Dancer, a Group 1 winner in Italy as a two-year-old, and Luca Cumani's Mons, one of the best of the previous year's juveniles, although time was beginning to show them as a moderate bunch. Then, just when we had something to be happy about, Santillana joined the team on the sidelines.

John Gosden can therefore look back on the first half of what should have been his best year since returning to England after a great career training in California as his unluckiest. So I felt it was unfair when an article written by David Ashforth appeared in *Sporting Life* rubbishing John as a trainer. Ashforth was merely putting into print some of the ideas of the whispering types who create so much jealousy and discontent in racing. There's always someone telling an owner to move his horse down the road, where the grass, as they say, is greener. In John's case he was supposed to have had unlimited chances and achieved nothing. As someone perhaps better qualified, seeing the horses every day, I would have to disagree. The middle-of-the-road horses in every stable are hard to win with. When your best half-dozen candidates all go wrong through no one's fault, it's hard to salvage much, but I'm sure John will be back to silence even the most unfair critics. He has won plenty of major Group races, especially in France, and he'll win plenty more.

7 The 2,000 Guineas

With the Guineas meeting next on the agenda, my thoughts inevitably turned to the imminent return of the big blue team from Dubai. Godolphin had been the sensation of 1995, winning the three biggest races of the European season – the Epsom Derby, the King George VI and Queen Elizabeth Diamond Stakes at Ascot and the Prix de l'Arc de Triomphe at Longchamp – with the same horse, Lammtarra, rightly regarded as Horse of the Year and now retired unbeaten to stud, a status restricted to very few top racehorses.

The Godolphin idea had been conceived of entirely by Sheikh Mohammed, the third of four brothers who rule the Emirate of Dubai. Most people find it hard enough to hold down a single job. Sheikh Mohammed, as well as heading two major racing entities, Darley Stud Management and Godolphin, has another time-consuming occupation: he is Defence Minister of the UAE. His duties commit him to the same round of visits and talks, conferences and worries as any other Minister of a Gulf nation. So, in an attempt to combine his two major responsibilities, Sheikh Mohammed set up Godolphin. The idea grew from his belief that it would be beneficial to the development of some young, very promising animals to be sheltered from the cold winters in Europe and to winter instead in the warmth of the Gulf. In this way, for six months each year, he could also, when in Dubai and not on overseas duty, monitor his horses' progress on a daily basis. As he says, 'I am the owner. I want to see my horses and have a say in how they are trained.' As a horseman with great experience in endurance races, and a man whose people bred the animals which were the fore-runners of the present thoroughbreds, it is hard to imagine anyone better qualified to help with his own horses' train-ing.

For Godolphin, he would provide the best staff, facilities and medical treatment. The entire programme would be based on conditioning to prepare the horses for the demands of the European season. In 1995, the major wins extended also to Japan and the United States. The Sheikh believes that Dubai is a strategic point from which to send horses east and west in the quest for major triumphs.

After Lammtarra's Arc, the news had come that one of Godolphin's major influences would be leaving. Jeremy Noseda had decided to try his luck as a trainer in California, and he made a fine start there with a very good strike-rate of winners to runners. In his place Sheikh Mohammed and his team recruited Tom Albertrani, an American who had been associated with the Cigar stable of Bill Mott in New York. Tom's wife Fonda was the reg-ular work rider for Cigar, and it was a bitter-sweet moment for the Albertranis when they watched Cigar win the Dubai World Cup. I have since got to know them better and they are a hard-working, knowledgeable couple who have fitted in well.

The Godolphin team is very tight-knit, loyal to their boss and to each other. The normal arrangement with horses and their running plans is that the trainer will suggest a race to the owner, and, within reason, expect him to approve the plan. Godolphin works to a different system. From the Boss, Sheikh Mohammed, down to the lads who ride the work, including the jockeys, all opinions are important. True, Sheikh Mohammed has the final say, but everyone else has the chance to offer their opinion and in some cases change the Boss's mind.

As one of the world's leading owners, and a noted horseman in his home country, Sheikh Mohammed has a wide knowledge of horses as individuals, and a vast experience in the selective area of thoroughbred breeding and racing. He has put together, with the help of his advisers, a wonderful band of mares and now he can rely on a greater proportion of home-bred horses. His idea to winter his young horses in Dubai was so different from anything attempted before it was viewed as unrealistic by many traditional racing people in Britain. The results, though, with such horses as Lammtarra, Moonshell, Balanchine, Mark Of Esteem and Halling, to name the best five advertisements for his visionary idea, have been spectacular. As the person lucky enough to ride them, I'd say the idea was brilliant. The care and skill with which it has been carried out, under the Boss's direction, by the Godolphin staff, has been mind-boggling.

Saeed bin Suroor looks more like a doctor or lawyer than a racehorse trainer, and when his appointment as Godolphin's new trainer was announced at the start of 1995 few could have expected the results to be as sensational as they proved. First, with Jeremy Noseda's and more recently with Tom Albertrani's help, Saeed has rapidly found his feet and has made an amazing impact. Saeed and Simon Crisford, once an assistant trainer to Sir Mark Prescott, form the main link with the Boss.

With three weeks to go to the Guineas, and knowing just how skilful the training team of Godolphin were at timing their horses' big-race preparation, I could not wait for them to arrive at Newmarket. They flew in from Dubai a few days before the Guineas meeting, and the press reaction was almost one of, 'Here they are, nobody else gets a chance. They'll win everything again.' Those of us closer to the team knew that this attitude was stupid and unrealistic. No Group 1 race is easily won. To win a Classic you need the best horse, in absolutely top shape, and we were still aware that the best colts from last year, Alhaarth and Beauchamp King, the horse who had recently surprised Mark Of Esteem in the Craven Stakes, would not be easily beaten in the 2,000 Guineas. As for the 1,000 Guineas, our top hope was Bint Shadayid and we never thought that she could beat Bosra Sham, the unbeaten filly of Henry Cecil's who had won her comeback race in the Fred Darling Stakes at Newbury with such style. We didn't have long to wait to find out.

The two horses which I had been most impressed with in Dubai, Mark Of Esteem and Mick's Love, were among the first of the Godolphin team to run, pretty much straight off the plane and almost before they had settled into the Moulton Paddocks stables where they and the rest of the team were to spend their summer. With four runners, two in one race, on the first day of the three-day Guineas meeting, the team had little time to spare. Mick's Love was first to run in the Newmarket Stakes and this looked quite a tough race. There was Henry Cecil's Clever Cliché, a good maiden winner at Nottingham and an intended Epsom Derby runner, and David Loder's Bahamian Knight, a horse David had always regarded highly. I had ridden plenty of winners both for David and Bahamian Knight's owner Edward St George and it was slightly ironic for me that, at the end of a tough race, Mick's Love beat Bahamian Knight in a photo-finish.

Again the cries came – 'Godolphin are doing it all over again' – but we did not make the winner's circle with our three other runners, Fatefully doing best with a second to Ta Rib in the fillies' maiden race. We were disappointed, especially to be beaten by five lengths, but when Ta Rib came out next time to win the French 1,000 Guineas, the Newmarket result was a little easier to accept. Still, with the big one to come, I was very happy about my chances in the 2,000 Guineas. Mark Of Esteem was clearly in great shape and I had been happy with his work in Dubai. But several questions remained. Did he have a turn of foot? If he did, how long would he be able to sustain it? Does he lengthen, and for how long? He had raced only twice before, finishing just behind Alhaarth at Newmarket the previous July, and then easily won a maiden race at Goodwood. We would have to find out everything else about him in the 2,000 Guineas.

I have ridden in plenty of dramatic races, but few which matched this 2,000 Guineas, which, for its unpredictability, the tightness of the finish, the controversy about the watering and another more personal controversy, was unique. There had been much talk, as before any big race, about where the best draw would be. Despite the cold weather in the spring there had been hardly any rain for a long time before the Guineas meeting. But whereas the ground for the trials meeting had been allowed to be very fast, it was decided to water quite heavily for the meeting two weeks later. In the event, many of the best-fancied horses were drawn middle to high, including Alhaarth, the hot favourite, Storm Trooper and Danehill Dancer, winners of two other trial races, and the very fast Royal Applause, who had been unbeaten as a two-year-old and had won the Middle Park Stakes.

I was drawn one off the rail in stall two and was happy to track the leader, World Premier, on that side, but he was already being outpaced by Royal Applause who went at 100 miles an hour up the middle of the track. All the time I felt I was going very easily, and had only to wait for a gap at the right moment to go on and win. At the two-furlong pole, I looked to my right, and noticed Beauchamp King and Alhaarth were almost in line with me, and that Royal Applause, just a few horse widths across, had already weakened. At this stage, Bijou d'Inde and Jason Weaver had just taken the lead and I noticed Even Top beginning a challenge on my outside.

When I got to the furlong pole I asked Mark Of Esteem for his effort, and he quickened far better than any other horse in the race. But then I had to ride him all the way to the line, and the others were coming back after him. All the jockeys on the front three horses were soon riding at full throttle and, at the line, Mark Of Esteem and Even Top were very close, just ahead of Bijou d'Inde with the rest a long way behind. Philip Robinson was convinced he had won. I was not sure, but as I'd hit the line I'd felt that I'd just held on. Because there was a new rule in operation we were made to stay out on the track instead of going back to unsaddle. We were out there for a long time, walking around for ages while a second print was scrutinised. It was strangely quiet, and then the announcement came: 'Result of the photo-finish.' Before the words came out, I quickly checked my number cloth – I was number seven. 'First, number seven.' We had won. On the spur of the moment I did a repeat of my Angel Cordero jump, which had been such a cause of enjoyment for everyone at the Arc when Lammtarra had won. The only trouble was, I simply hopped into the arms of John Davies, Godolphin's travelling head lad. John said, 'You'd better get back on.' I was chuffed to bits, and thought, 'Great, I've finally won the one race I've always wanted to win, the 2,000 Guineas.' It was the race my dad had won on Bolkonski and Wollow all those years ago and the first 2,000 Guineas for Godolphin.

It was then that people started to realise that, technically, a rule of racing had been broken. No jockey is allowed to dismount and come into contact with anyone before entering the unsaddling enclosure. But I was only in that position because they had made us stay out on the track. I believe that action could have been dangerous for the welfare of both horses, and the tension that being in an unaccustomed place caused us added to the difficulties. The 'no-contact' rule was originally framed in the days when cameras and television were still many years off. A jockey could ride in a race without some of the required weight and have it slipped back to him as he returned to the weighing room to weigh in. But, nowadays, to slip someone a big piece of lead, enough to make a difference in a photo-finish, is not a very practical idea.

I was very surprised when Mark Tompkins, the trainer of Even Top, went on television the following day and said that I was unprofessional. He admitted that he would not be appealing the result, but said that he reckoned he had grounds for doing so, suggesting by implication that it was only because he was such a good sport that he did not intend appealing. Amid all the controversy, I was reassured when Mr David Pipe, the Jockey Club's Director of Publicity, declared that in his view racing should be fun and that my action in jumping off had shown just how delighted I had been. I was only showing my excitement, pleasure for the Godolphin people, especially Sheikh Mohammed, and my relief that I had not been beaten in a tight finish in a third Guineas after Grand Lodge and Balanchine.

That flying Angel Cordero leap cost me a lecture in the stewards' room and a £500 fine, but that was nothing compared to the treatment given to all three jockeys who had tried so hard to win the first Classic of the year, and to give the owners and trainers the great distinction and commercial advantage of collecting a Classic race. We were all found guilty by the stewards of excessive use of the whip. Jason was banned for two days, Philip for four and I got an eight-day ban, to my absolute amazement. I'd had to ride all the way to the line. This was a Classic race. I am not known as a jockey hard on his horses, and in order to keep him going, I did exceed the official maximum of ten strokes with the whip. I understand it was supposed to be sixteen, and the stewards said that I had hit the horse out of time with his action. When you hit a horse quickly, as I did, you do not make as hard a contact as someone hitting every three or four strides with full force. I used the whip to encourage him to keep going. I may have given him a stroke too many, but the fact was that at the end of one mile of Newmarket we had won by less than an inch. I felt I deserved credit. Instead, I was banned for eight days for having tried too hard. Add to that the criticism by Mark Tompkins that I had been 'most unprofessional' and you will understand why my fifth Classic win seemed to have exploded in my face, especially when it seems that non-trying jockeys get away with a small fine. In my case, an eight-day ban can cost me a lot of money. It did.

The next day I got up at seven a.m. to rush down for the papers. Normally, on a Sunday, the racing papers are not published, but this was 1,000 Guineas day, so I couldn't wait to read about my 2,000 Guineas win, one of the dream days of my career so far. But instead of great headlines about what I believed was one of my best big-race rides, the stories were all about my riding ban for use of the whip, and about jumping off and the chance of there being an objection about my flying jump. Then they talked about the bans for the first three jockeys and it was as if we were butchers. I cannot imagine winning a big race and having so much disappointment afterwards.

So, for me, one of the best wins of this or any year was spoilt by some petty stories in the press and the remarks of Mark Tompkins. I was not trying to cheat the system, merely showing my happiness at winning. It seemed a lot of people jumped on the band-waggon. When Mark Tompkins was interviewed on Channel 4 the next day, I did understand how he must have felt at missing the 2,000 Guineas by such a small margin. I felt nothing against him but did feel that it was a little below the belt when he said I should go and work in Chipperfield's Circus. What he probably didn't know was that my mother came from a circus family. He also said I was less professional than most apprentices.

All those remarks really hurt me. I am employed by Sheikh Mohammed and John Gosden and if anyone should complain of my actions, when I jump off a horse, for example, it should be them. If they disapproved I am sure they would have told me by now. What Mark Tompkins seemed to forget was that most of the top jockeys spend almost as much time on horses as they do with their feet on the ground. They feel for the horses, and I reckon I know which horse it is safe to try the jump from, and from which it is not.

When things turn against you, it is important that the people you work for are on your side. I am lucky that John Gosden has become not just a boss, but a good friend, and Sheikh Mohammed and the rest of the Godolphin people are also always there for me. After reading the papers on the Sunday morning of the Guineas meeting, I went to the track in a terrible frame of mind. I was very sour and felt that my skill and maybe even my integrity were being questioned. As a jockey you can only try to the best of your ability. Later in the summer, Mick Kinane made the wrong choice about which horse to ride in the Irish Derby. Zagreb, the horse he could have ridden for his own stable, won by six lengths. Mick had preferred to take an outside ride on Dr Massini, the horse who had been favourite for Epsom before going wrong. I know I would find it very hard to take any outside ride rather than stay with Godolphin, or John, and, if they are not involved, Ian Balding or David Loder, if they wanted me. Matty Cowing my agent believes you have to stay with your people, and I go along with that. You have to be loyal to your people. They stand by you when you need them most, and in my case I want to use my skills for the benefit of those people who use me.

People often use Lester Piggott as an example of someone whose loyalty was questionable. Sometimes, of course, he made unpopular decisions and his search for the best possible Derby ride in the days when he dominated the race occasionally put someone's nose out of joint. But the example of his split with Sir Noël Murless, which led to his association with Vincent O'Brien which lasted until the end of the two men's careers, was more about the rights of jockeys than loyalty. Lester is very loyal to the people he values and while I was just starting on my career he gave me many opportunities.

After the 1996 Irish Derby, the press were full of sympathy for Mick Kinane and almost made more of his bad luck than the brilliant win of Zagreb and the great training achievement of Dermot Weld, who has had Mick as his stable jockey for eleven years. I'd hate to think I'd have missed a winner like that, but if you do you just shrug your shoulders and go on to the next race. Mick's a pro and knew that later in the year he'd be back on Zagreb again.

I haven't been with John Gosden anywhere near as long as eleven years. Indeed, I had not even made that first trip to England when Mick and Dermot began their partnership, but I have known John long enough to be glad to call him my friend and happy to tell everyone else, if not him, that he is my hero. He's the first person I would go to for advice about anything concerning all walks of life, not just racing and riding but personal things, too.

Anyway, I arrived at the track on 1,000 Guineas day in a bad mood. I was riding Bint Shadayid in the big race. With Bosra Sham under a cloud because she had been treated for a bruised foot almost right up to the time of the race, we were hoping for the best. But Bosra Sham, thanks to her trainer Henry Cecil and probably just as much to the stable blacksmith, kept her unbeaten record with a brave effort. We ran on to finish third, a good achievement with Bint Shadayid, who is a bit of a nervous filly. I hardly spoke to anyone that day, and when Tony Stafford of the *Daily Telegraph* suggested we do a small piece together for the paper under a contract I have with them, I left him in no doubt that I had other things on my mind. Not a good day. But then it isn't surprising as I'm not a robot, but an individual with feelings and emotions. I work hard, but I can get upset. I'm just myself. Luckily, time heals, and nothing heals you quicker than the anticipation of a big win later in the year.

As I left Newmarket to go home after the 1,000 Guineas, apart from the satisfaction of finishing placed in another Classic race there was also one good win to enjoy. In the race before the 1,000 Guineas, the Pretty Polly Stakes, I rode a filly called Pricket. She had been unimpressive on the sand in Dubai, but the Godolphin team were hoping she would still show herself useful when she got back to England, as she had won her only race at Sandown the previous August very nicely. We thought she would have needed to improve to win this Listed race as she was meeting Magnificient Style, a stable-companion of Bosra Sham. Magnificient Style, owned by Mr Fustok, had won her maiden race at Kempton by six lengths from a decent animal of Luca Cumani's, Migwar, so it was hardly surprising that she started favourite at Newmarket. The race, however, proved no contest. I was always cantering on Pricket, let her take the lead at the furlong pole and, once she went clear, I never saw another horse. She had plenty in hand at the finish, where she was five lengths clear of Faraway Waters. Magnificient Style was only third. When Magnificient Style easily won York's Musidora Stakes from Sil Sila – who later won the French Oaks – it became clear that Pricket was the one to beat in the Oaks at Epsom.

Of course, after my ban I would not be in York for the spring meeting, which is often such a good guide to the Epsom Classics. The Dante Stakes, and the Glasgow Stakes, which are both over ten and a half furlongs, are especially good guides to the Epsom Derby. While the other jockeys were building up their book of rides for York, I had a couple of days' action at Chester and then went away to Amalfi, in Southern Italy, for a few days' holiday with Catherine. We stayed there for four days, and it was great to get out in some warm sunshine, instead of the endlessly cold spring back in England. The holiday did not start too well. We missed our flight by two minutes. The lady from British Airways told us the flight was closed, but there was still half an hour before take-off time. So instead of going direct to Naples we had to fly from Gatwick to Paris, take another flight from Paris to Rome and a third local flight from Rome to Naples. We finally got there at eight p.m. about ten hours later than we had expected. For most of the four days, I took the chance to rest, sleeping for up to fifteen hours a day.

I returned home relaxed and recharged for the rest of the season. Back in England, I found that Peter Burrell, my marketing manager, had arranged for me to help promote the Vodafone Derby meeting. The racecourse at Epsom and the race sponsors were anxious for the race to get as much coverage in the press and broadcasting media as possible, as it was facing strong competition from the Euro '96 soccer championships. With England's first game in the championships starting at Wembley ten minutes after the off-time at Epsom, the course's worries were understandable, but with, I hope, some help from me, the race attracted a crowd of 56,000.

As part of my round of visits to radio stations and other media appointments around the country, I was pleased to call in on the England football team's training base at Bisham Abbey for a photo call. I did a few pictures with my friend David Platt, whom I have known for some time as he is married to the sister of Nicky Vaughan, John Gosden's travelling head lad. I was delighted when in 1995 David signed for my team, Arsenal, and he and the England squad did a great job in Euro '96.

I reckon that the Derby crowd was pretty good in the circumstances, and that the decision to retain Saturday as Derby day for the immediate future is probably the right one. A Saturday Derby means that people who have to work during the week can attend. Also, children will not have to be in school. I know that when young people get the chance to attend major events they are likely to become enthusiasts. There is no question that if the race reverted to the traditional date there would be fewer young people and families attending. With an entry fee of £10 for a car on the Downs in the middle of the course, the Derby is an inexpensive weekend venue for ordinary families.

I was not under tremendous pressure at the Derby because I was riding an outsider, Shantou. He is a well-bred horse and I knew he would last the mile and a half. He had run a good race at Newmarket on his reappearance and had then gone on to win a mile maiden at Sandown. On Derby day itself his odds came down from 40–1 to 25–1, so obviously a few people fancied him. It was definitely a pretty open contest. Shantou ran a hell of a race, putting in his best right at the end and came in third. I was delighted.

Before the race, I had held out higher hopes for Pricket in the Oaks. She had come to Epsom as favourite after winning the Pretty Polly Stakes at Newmarket in very impressive style. I must say I thought I had an excellent chance of winning my third Oaks in a row. It was not to be. Pricket never fired, and although she came second, she was beaten by nine lengths by the Henry Cecil-trained Lady Carla, with Geoff Wragg's Mezzogiorno third. Pricket did not give her best that day. Oh well, that's the luck of racing!

8 Injury

The Chinese, I'm told, have a saying, 'the bigger the front, the bigger the back'. I suppose that means the greater the success you are enjoying, the bigger the fall is likely to be. For me, two days in June 1996 certainly showed the truth of that. It all started so quietly. A morning of riding work, starting very early with Godolphin, getting some of the Royal Ascot horses ready, and then the prospect of about nine or ten rides, split between Yarmouth in the afternoon and Kempton in the evening. Because of the distance from Yarmouth to Kempton I'd have to catch a plane and as I would be riding the next day at Newbury, I'd arranged to stay that night at the Kingsclere stables with trainer Ian Balding so that I would not have to go back late that night to Newmarket and re-trace my steps back to Newbury the next day. Ian was another of my regular trainers to be suffering. With the awful winter, Ian's stables simply hadn't fired. At the time, Ian had won only four races. You had to sympathise with him.

Tony Stafford of the *Daily Telegraph* was going to Yarmouth, and he broke his journey from Hertfordshire to pick me up. We went through a few things, talking about the Derby of the week before, and Tony was keen to find out what I thought about my rides for the day, in case I could give him a winner. I'd had a look in the paper when I'd got back from the work and before taking a quick nap and I thought the best chance I had at Yarmouth was probably Brian Gubby's horse Easy Dollar, who was going in a three-horse race over six furlongs. They say jockeys are not the greatest tipsters in the world, although I don't really agree with that as some of the newspaper guys must make their readers broke. This time, though, I was a little off the mark. Easy Dollar, 6–4 joint-favourite, trailed home last of three. My other three rides at Yarmouth all won, and to make Tony's day, I had three more at Kempton that night. It was the first time I'd ridden six winners in a day: my best before had been five.

With six wins in a day behind me, I was on top of the world. People might think it's nothing special, and that it's the horses that do the work. But the fact is you have to go out there, often encouraging a horse, who might not be too keen, to do his best and get as near to winning as possible, for the sake of his owner and trainer who invest so much time and money into his welfare.

So, leaving Kempton that night, I allowed myself just a little smile of satisfaction. What with my big suspension after the 2,000 Guineas win on Mark Of Esteem and one or two other setbacks, I had been trailing Pat Eddery, who had been going really well since coming back fresh for the fight at the start of the turf season. His agent and brother-in-law, Terry Ellis, had been his usual busy self, keeping Pat's name in the trainers' minds, and Pat as ever did the business. But now, with John Gosden coming into form, David Loder's team showing signs of getting going and Godolphin also warming up some nice two-year-olds to go with their established stars, I was hoping to cut into Pat's lead.

Ten rides in a day, following an early start on the gallops, is quite draining, so I wasn't sorry when Ian allowed me to miss first lot and let me lie in. Ever since Ian stood by me in those dark days three years ago, I've enjoyed my occasional visits to Kingsclere even though each time I have to sit through yet another playing of the Mill Reef video, which must be wearing out by now, with all the times Ian plays it. Still, no wonder he's so proud of that great horse. Ian's wife, Emma, son Andrew and daughter Clare, who now does such a good job in the Sports Department of BBC Radio Five Live, are all very knowledgeable and great company. Matty knows that even if one of Ian's horses might not have the most obvious chance in a race and we've been offered other rides, I'd rather be on Ian's horse. Loyalty deserves to be repaid.

Ian woke me with the papers at around eight thirty a.m. I enjoyed reading about 'Frankie's six-timer' and then we went out with the horses for second lot. It was a beautiful summer's day and I wore a T-shirt, jeans and my racing boots, as I hadn't brought any of my own riding-out gear. I rode four of Ian's nicer two-year-olds. I was pleased to see that they all seemed to be coming into form and looking quite well just when it was needed. It was good to see Ian looking a little happier. After riding out, we went back to the house to change for the races. I was very hopeful as I had some nice rides booked.

Going into the paddock before the Listed race for fillies I remember feeling very happy. I was very philosophical that day, in relaxed mode. As I got to the paddock I remember seeing Damien Oliver. It was a surprise to see him there. He's Australian and about my age. He's the jockey sensation of the moment in Australia and rides incredibly well. I told him I'd have a chat with him in the weighing room after the race. I was riding a grey filly, Shawanni, for the Godolphin team. I'd ridden her before and she hadn't been too bad, but she's one of those fillies you wouldn't like to upset. She's one of those girls, she could be anything, she's gonna be trouble!

When I got on her she froze and would not go anywhere. I took my feet out of the irons and told her lad to take a half-turn behind one of the other horses as she did not seem to want to be in front by herself. So the lad took the half-turn and she froze again. The next minute she reared up. Normally, when a horse freezes you have one or two seconds to decide whether you want to jump off. She went straight over on to her back with me on top.

At that stage I had only one thought: 'She's going to squash me.' Shawanni just veered off a little to the left, though, and landed to my right. I was lucky, otherwise she would have smashed my pelvis. As I landed, I felt a tremendous pain. In that moment I couldn't really pick out where the pain was coming from. But I felt really faint. Within fifteen seconds I'd come to terms with the situation, realising I could not move my left arm. The first thing I discovered was that I could move my fingers, which was a great relief, but when I tried to move my elbow, I was in real pain. I had landed on the tarmac and because, before, I'd broken my right elbow, I knew straight away that the other elbow was broken. A few people came over straight away and they all stood there. I was in pain and obviously in shock. Jane Chapple-Hyam, the wife of Peter Chapple-Hyam, who trains at Manton for Robert Sangster, asked them to take the pin out of my collar. Jockeys usually wear a pin and Jane was worried it might stop my breathing properly.

Hardly anyone realised that I'd done some serious damage. Even the doctor came and said it was probably 'only severe bruising'. I just said: 'I broke my elbow.' Eventually, the ambulance people put me onto a stretcher and were going to take me into the medical room. I said, 'Take me straight to hospital', but still we couldn't leave until another ambulance was sent for. We waited half an hour for the ambulance to come, and it took another half-hour to get to Reading District Hospital. Typically, when I got to the Casualty Department, I was not the only person waiting to be seen. Everyone in the Reading area seemed to have chosen that afternoon to get an injury of some sort and it was an hour and a half before I was seen.

In that time I was in such pain that I thought I would pass out. To forget the pain I tried to go to sleep. Eventually, I was taken for an X-ray and only then, when the doctor saw my X-ray, which showed the main bone forcing down and right through the joint, did he say, 'Give that man an injection.' I was wheeled down to a nice private ward with a TV. Richard Dodds was the consultant looking after me. He said that, if I was happy, he would operate on me in the morning. Apart from my family, the closest people to me in England are John Gosden and Barney Curley. I spoke to John and he arranged everything. Catherine came down later with Andy, my driver. They stayed in a nearby bed and breakfast, which the nurses found for them, and came to see me in the morning. John was there, too.

Operations scare me, especially the anaesthetic, when you never know if you are going to wake up afterwards. When John came in he looked very worried and pale.

Probably, he was more worried than me. I was told everything would be all right and I was reassured when I saw the
anaesthetist. I had played football with him in a charity
match a year earlier. He put the anaesthetic in my arm, and
I felt myself go. It must have been just before I fell asleep
when I remember saying: 'I love you all.'

I woke up at around four p.m. and my arm really hurt. I
was disoriented, because of the painkillers, I suppose.
Barney came to see me, with Catherine and Andy. John
stayed until nine to see Richard Dodds, who told him
everything had gone okay. The whole thing at the hospital
impressed me, and one aspect I hadn't really expected was
just how nice the nurses were. What they have to go
through, working with fifty people in the ward all with
different problems, yet always they seem to have a smile on
their faces. When I got home, I sent them a signed picture.

Because I had had a broken elbow before, I realised it
would take a long time, probably three to four months, for
me to recover properly. It could not have come at a worse
time, with Royal Ascot the following week. When I got
home on the Monday I had to come to terms with the fact
that I would be out for a while. I had a bad night and, the
next morning, the only thing I had to look forward to was
watching Italy play West Germany in the Euro '96 football
championships later that day.

It was the first day of Royal Ascot and Colin Rate, my
best friend, came to watch the meeting on TV with me, and
other people kept popping in to see how I was. I said that
if some of my horses won at Ascot I wouldn't get up. Well,
the first race came on TV and Charnwood Forest, who I
would have ridden, bolted in. It was such a shock. It was
like when something suddenly hits you in the stomach. We
had a late lunch and everyone really took the mickey out of

me. At first it was hard to digest – all I could do was glance at my arm and think 'You'll live'. I was disappointed for a different reason later in the meeting when Mark Of Esteem ran so badly. The St James's Palace Stakes was for me the race of the meeting and so it proved with Bijou d'Inde getting back under a great ride from Jason to beat Ashkalani.

That night, Catherine had invited her friends Katie and Julian for dinner, so I was to have my cooking hat on. I called my sister to ask her for a special pasta recipe. I cooked the pasta and made a sauce with sausage, onion, bacon and tomato, and served it with lots of Parmesan. The food was great, but Italy only managed a 0–0 draw. Once everyone realised Italy had been eliminated from the championships, the phone started to ring with so-called friends offering plenty of abuse. Italy were out and Charnwood Forest had won at Ascot. No wonder I got up and went to bed early!

The Wednesday at Royal Ascot had never held great promise for me, but I had been meant to ride the French-trained filly Tulipa for Sheikh Mohammed in the Ribblesdale Stakes in the first race on Gold Cup day. When she won for the André Fabre stable that was disappointment enough, and then, of course, came the race I had been looking forward to for a long time. The Gold Cup might be over two and a half miles, but it is Royal Ascot's own special 'Classic' race. I have always enjoyed riding in the Gold Cup, and won it twice on Drum Taps for Lord Huntingdon. Few horses stay two and a half miles, and for Godolphin's Classic Cliché to win he would not only need to last out the trip, but have too much class for Double Trigger, the previous year's Gold Cup winner. I was pretty confident Classic Cliché would stay the distance, as he is such a relaxed horse, and as a St Leger winner I was certain he'd have the better finishing speed, but, at the same time, I knew the fast ground was not ideal for him.

Of course, Classic Cliché just sat on the tail of Double Trigger, who made the running, and, when Mick Kinane asked Classic Cliché, he won well. I was already feeling very sorry for myself. Once the TV transmission ended, I went to a local bookmaker to see the last two races. Godolphin won the Chesham Stakes, too, with the new-comer Shamikh, so that meant I'd missed three winners in a single day at Ascot. I had been thinking for some time that I'd have a great chance of winning the trophy for top jockey at the meeting. Three wins in a day would almost certainly (as it turned out they would) have meant that I and not Mick Kinane would have won the London Clubs (formerly Ritz Club) Trophy for the first time at Royal Ascot. To win any trophy at one of the major meetings is rewarding, and I've twice been top jockey at the Glorious Goodwood summer meeting. So to miss this trophy and the prestige that goes with it hit me more than the loss of income.

I knew there would be plenty more chances to win races at Royal Ascot and fulfil that ambition, but I still felt very sorry for myself. Poor Catherine, she was being so nice to me, but I thought, 'There's only one man for this job', and called Barney, asking him to come round for half an hour to help get my head right.

On the Friday morning, the newspapers all agreed once more on the main topic. It was not so much how well Classic Cliché had done to win the Gold Cup; instead most of them seemed to be saying that Jason had not gone fast enough on Double Trigger. When it comes to running against a class horse like Classic Cliché, I believe that if Jason had gone any faster, it would have made no difference

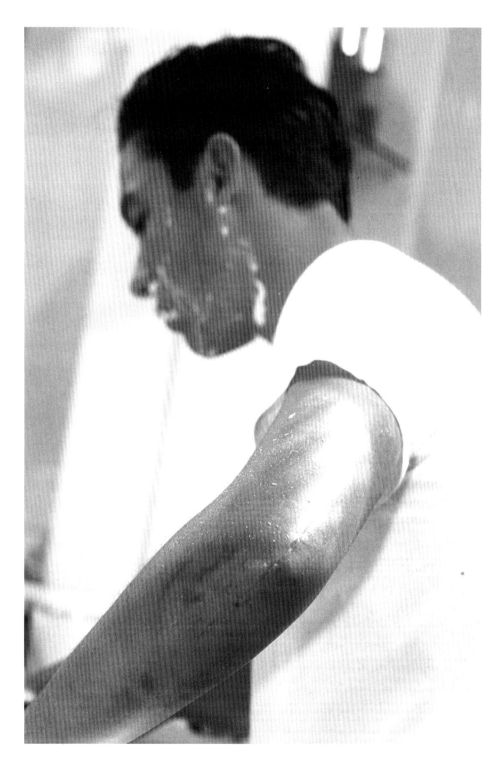

My injured elbow.

With Sheikh Mohammed and his trainer, Saeed bin Suroor, in the background.

Halling winning the International Juddmonte Stakes at York.

Back in the limelight.

Indiscreet winning in the style of a Group horse for '97.

to the winner, but Double Trigger could have finished a lot further behind.

After reading the papers with all the Ascot coverage, I had a sudden thought. It looked a very nice day and as I had been a pain in the ass ever since I'd got back from hospital, I thought Catherine deserved a break from me telling her 'Do this, do that'. It occurred to me that it would be good to go racing, to help support John Gosden with Shantou. He, after all, had been third for me in the Epsom Derby only thirteen days before. John had been so good after the accident, I wanted to show him that I still considered myself part of the team. Then I thought that, if I was going to Royal Ascot, I'd like to wear a morning suit. As a jockey at Ascot you come in, ride in some races and then leave, so all the jockeys just wear normal suits. I tried to think who might be able to lend me a morning suit and immediately thought of my good friend Bruce Raymond, who I reckoned was a similar height and size to me, and likely to have a suitable outfit.

I called Bruce and asked him if he was going to Ascot that day and was relieved when he said he wasn't. Then I asked if I could borrow his suit and, when he agreed, I had it collected and tried it on. It was a perfect fit all over. We cut an arm off one of my shirts and it wasn't too bad getting changed, even though it was awkward dressing with the arm in plaster. Ever since the accident Catherine had stopped being a fiancée and had become a nurse, something which she knows about as her sister is a nurse. She had to wash me, dress me and everything. I was like a little boy being dressed by his mother for his first day at school. Once I was dressed, I really got quite excited. I was going to a big race meeting for the first time purely as a spectator.

I went in the car with John and his wife Rachel. Even

travelling there had a different feeling. Normally, while I am being driven to the track for Royal Ascot I would be looking at the papers, scanning the races from A to Z, looking for clues as to how to get the best results from my rides, noting which horses I thought might make the running, which would be the ones to follow in the big fields. Now I simply closed my eyes and slept, without a care in the world.

I was looking forward to another unusual treat: lunch at the races. John and Rachel had been invited to lunch with Grant Pritchard-Gordon, the racing manager for the big Saudi Arabian owner Prince Khalid Abdulla, who has quite a few horses with John, and I gate-crashed lunch with them. Luckily, there was plenty of room around the table and it was a good way to escape the crush of a very big crowd. The most enjoyable thing was that I just had lunch and was one of the public in my top hat and tails. I felt that everyone was staring at me; a few of them must have spotted who I was. The one difficult thing was when I went to the toilet and was trying to unzip my trousers with my one free hand, someone tapped me on the shoulder. I hope he didn't think I was being rude when I couldn't shake his hand.

It was a great joy going to the races, especially once we started moving around the track and I realised how many people wanted to talk to me and wish me well. Popularity may be something which you can be lucky enough to have for a short time, but I did feel that day that people were happy to see me. I went in to the weighing room of course and realised, perhaps for the first time, what a rush it is for everyone. No one had much time to talk to me; they were all concentrating on getting ready for their next ride. I did feel a bit of an outsider. It was strange, but the atmosphere was pretty good just the same. I stayed most of the day with John and I was grabbed at one stage by Julian Wilson to have a small interview for BBC TV. I told him all about the accident and said that Royal Ascot is our own Olympics, with its tradition, passion and professionalism, and with the Royal family also there the whole time. After what I had read in the morning about Jason I told Julian I thought he had ridden the best race of his life on Bijou d'Inde in the St James's Palace Stakes on Tuesday. Yet just two days later they are criticising him, when all that happened was that he was beaten by a better horse. I was glad I stood up for him on TV.

While I was at Ascot I bumped into one of John's new owners, Ronnie Wood, who is one of the legends of pop music, having played with the Rolling Stones. I have never met anyone so enthusiastic about racing. He's experienced so much success, but because I had done well in another activity in which he is starting to get involved, he was looking up to me. It was a strange feeling. Then we were in the paddock with Shantou. I wanted him to do well in the King Edward VII Stakes, as he is one of my babies and my ride when I come back. That's something I could relate to. I must say it was more nerve-racking watching him run than being out there riding him. There was nothing I could do to help him.

I bumped into Sheikh Mohammed. I hadn't seen him since the accident. He told me they had retired Shawanni because she had become a bit of a handful. I told him, 'It was just one of those things.' He said he missed me riding at Ascot and that he was really sorry about what had happened. I told him, 'It's not your fault. Just one of the hazards of the job.' Luckily, one that doesn't happen very often. While it all might look glamorous, it can be a risky business riding such powerful horses.

Afterwards, I went back to the weighing room. I'd already said hello to everyone earlier on, and now I was really an outsider. I had to step back and ask myself, 'Is this really what I do every day?' It looked so crazy and disorganised, and I wondered whether it was just because it was Royal Ascot or was it like that every day? I realised that it was just the same as always: riding your last horse of the day, gathering up your stuff and sprinting for a car or a plane to get to the night meeting, keeping a ridiculously tight schedule.

Being with John that day also gave me a little insight into how things are for trainers and owners after a race, especially when a horse runs less well than expected. I could see from John's face that he was disappointed by Shantou. He hadn't got the best of runs and was in a poor position turning for home. Watching the race unfold, I felt helpless, not being able to do anything about it. He ran on at the finish for third. Normally, a jockey will come back, explain to the owner and trainer what happened, why it went wrong and then walk away to prepare for the next ride. The trainer has to start thinking out his reasons for the result not going his and the owner's way. For the first time, I saw the effect losing has on the owner and the trainer. Mick Kinane had left us and we were there going over everything in our minds. The jockey had done what he was paid for, the trainer is left with the post mortem, the new plan of how to get the best out of the horse on behalf of the owner.

I see the jockey's role, especially when he rides regularly for a stable, as something like that of a racing driver. When drivers compete in a Grand Prix or any race, they report back on all aspects of the car's performance so that the technical people can make adjustments to get a better result next time. I might say, 'Try a new distance – he wants further or shorter, try running him from the front.' Fine-tuning really.

Now we were back in our car, expecting a normal journey, but we had forgotten about the infamous M25 Friday car park. John had gone off with Sheikh Mohammed for a meeting, so I was with Rachel in the car. At the M3 junction with the M25, we looked right and the traffic going towards the Dartford tunnel was solid; we looked left to go north and it was solid. We went left and it took us three hours to go just over ninety miles. I called Catherine from the car and said I'd had a good day, but told her not to cook: 'Book a table at Number Nine,' which is a restaurant in Newmarket. She'd done enough all week nursing me.

I enjoyed the chat with Rachel going back to Newmarket. She's very smart and knowledgeable and interesting to speak to. I hope she wasn't bored listening to my life story. The next day I saw England play Spain on TV and when it came to the penalty shoot out I had tears in my eyes. I was scared for my friend David Platt when he had to take his penalty. I thought, 'You've got to be brave in front of 80,000 people and many millions more watching, like me, on TV.' As ever, David came up with the goods, and to see Stuart Pearce's face after his penalty had helped England win was one of the most emotional moments for me in sport. Afterwards, when I thought of it, the boys were not just taking their penalties, they were taking them for all of us who wanted them to win. What a responsibility. Imagine Gareth Southgate after the semi-final. If I get it wrong on the track, it's a loss to the people involved in the race and the betting public. A missed penalty affects almost everyone in the country. Even Henry Cecil watched the game. It was quite funny to think he'd never seen Gazza play before. Henry thought he played well and looked a good player. He knows more about roses – and horses, of course.

The following Sunday I suffered another blow. Colin telephoned to say he wanted to come round to see me. Colin and his girlfriend, Alex, had been with Catherine and me on holiday in Switzerland at the start of the year. At the time she'd seemed very happy and the four of us had had a great time. We were all looking forward to November when they planned to be married and I was going to be Colin's Best Man. But as soon as he arrived at my house I realised something was wrong: Alex had said she didn't want to get married. Colin was so sad, shattered really, and I could see the look of shock on his face. The day before he'd thought everything was going well for him and in the space of one minute his whole life was messed up. Now the tables were turned between us and this time it was me who had to be his big brother, unlike when I first came to Newmarket and Colin looked after me. He came and stayed with me for a while to get his head right. Gradually, he began to feel better. Life goes on, but it can be cruel all right.

9 Road to Recovery

The first two weeks of my own recovery seemed never-ending. The time went so slowly and the pain and discomfort were with me all the time. Then it was time to contact Mr Dodds, the consultant, to get a progress report on my elbow. He arranged to see me and I went to the hospital with Catherine and Andy. I wanted Catherine with me because ten years earlier, when the plaster had come off after I'd broken the other elbow, I'd taken one look at it and fainted. I wanted her there because I thought I might faint again, and was worried how it would look.

There were two or three people in the waiting room, all with plaster on various limbs. It was soon my moment of truth. A nurse very carefully removed the plaster and, to my relief and pride almost, I didn't faint. I was pretty pleased with myself. Like a proud little boy who doesn't cry after a bad fall. But I was surprised when I actually saw the arm. It looked awful. There was a woman there talking to her husband and she looked as though she would faint when she saw my arm. They were all trying not to look at me.

Then we went into Mr Dodds's office and he organised another X-ray. When eventually the pictures came back, he said, 'Everything's going to plan,' and told me that the bone should heal in another four weeks. It seems any bone takes six weeks to recover from a break: a broken leg requires twice as long. He said that the wounds seemed in good shape and that I could keep the plaster off. He told me to do everything very gently, never to force movement. So far, so good.

The next morning I made my first visit to one of my regular stopping-off points in Newmarket. Any jockey who needs to lose a couple of pounds has a number of alternatives. Some have saunas at home, others use the ones at racecourses, but I find it much better to use the facilities available at the Bedford Lodge hotel, which is just along from Stanley House stables, where John Gosden trains, on Bury Road in Newmarket. So I went to the swimming pool there and saw a few of the ladies who regularly use the Bedford Lodge sauna. They all wished me a 'speedy recovery'. It was obviously too soon to do anything there, but as I had been eating more than usual in those early days after the accident, I decided to walk the two miles from the town and across Newmarket heath to my house in The Drive. At that time of day, most of the horses have finished their exercise on the gallops and are already eating their late breakfast, but a few stragglers were still around, and it felt very strange to be on foot. I had become an outsider, but everyone who noticed me said 'hello', so that helped me believe I was indeed a jockey. Later that day I went to see John, and when he saw my arm he seemed very shocked. He told me to put some

Arnica on it to help reduce the bruising.

I thought that my recovery would be speeded up if I could get out into some sunshine, so I arranged to go on 25 June with Catherine to Gran Canaria, where my dad has an apartment. Before I went, the doctor said: 'The elbow is locked, so you have to unlock it. But don't try to unlock it with pressure. It's a very long, slow process.' At that stage, I could almost touch my nose with a finger, but I couldn't straighten my arm, which was locked in an L-shape. The only thing that concerned me was the scar from the operation, as I didn't want it to come open while I was away. But when he inspected it, Mr Dodds said that it seemed to have healed nicely and should be all right.

So we flew out to Gran Canaria and every day I spent the afternoons by the toddlers' pool. The first few days, I would go in and crouch under the water and do a 'pretend' breast-stroke, only gently at first, just to get the arm moving. By the third day, I had a little more confidence in my elbow and could use my strength to float on the surface. So much of it was to do with confidence. When you have an injury like that, you are always afraid that something will go wrong, and the injury will get worse. In my case, everything was going fine and by the fifth day there I was able to go into the proper adult pool and swim about forty lengths, each of which was probably twenty metres or so. The climate in Gran Canaria is always ideal, and whether it's June or December, the temperature seems to vary by only a couple of degrees, from between around twenty-six and twenty-eight degrees Celsius. So the sea is beautiful and by now every afternoon I was going to the sea with my dad and basically working. We'd swim a bit, and then float for a long while. To float in a wavy sea takes much more work than in a swimming pool, so you have to move your arms under the water to keep afloat. The elbow would therefore be kept moving, while the sea itself helps reduce the pressure on the arm. While we floated, for about thirty minutes each day, we would chat about life and racing, of course. After six or seven days, I was able to cope with swimming fifty lengths in the morning and another fifty in the afternoon and I could see that every day the arm was getting better. By now I could touch my shoulder and my arm was getting quite strong.

In the flat, my dad has a satellite TV and it has the BBC World Television channel, with Teletext. I used to punch up Teletext each night to see the racing results back in England, and I remember waiting anxiously on the Saturday of the Coral-Eclipse Stakes for the result. Eventually, the name Halling flashed up as the winner, with Bijou d'Inde second. I was angry and frustrated at missing a Group 1 win on a favourite horse of mine. I rushed out to the pool and did another twenty-five lengths to calm myself down. I was pleased he'd won, but at the same time I felt frustrated that I hadn't been involved in his big win.

By the tenth day it was obvious that there was great improvement in my arm. Now I was keen to start bringing the muscles in the arm back into shape. I wanted to get a spongeball to grip to work the muscles, but couldn't find one in Gran Canaria, so instead I got a sponge and began squeezing that the whole time. That helped, too, and I thought it was probably the right time to come home to see the doctor. It was still less than four weeks since my accident, so when I called him to say that I wanted him to see how much the injury had improved, he wasn't too keen. He said: 'You should come to see me after six weeks, as it takes that long for the bones to heal.' I still pressed him to let me come, saying, 'You want to look at this' and eventually he agreed. I was convinced the healing process was pretty advanced. He examined my arm, said that it looked great and then sent me for an X-ray. The X-ray proved a great disappointment to me, though. You could detect a line where the bones were put together – there were still signs of calcification. I was very disappointed. I had been taking calcium tablets while I was in Gran Canaria and eating lots of Parmesan (which also contains calcium), so I'd expected it all to have healed already.

My return to England was timed to coincide with a nice invitation I had received from the Ritz Club, who were going to present trophies to several sportsmen, each of whom were reckoned to be the sportsman of the various decades. I was the sportsman of the 90s, rather premature as we're only just over halfway there – and had someone kidnapped Eric Cantona? Gary Lineker was the man of the 80s; my great racing hero Lester Piggott was the man of the 70s; Henry Cooper, who had knocked Muhammad Ali down in a world title bout, was the man of the 60s; Sir Stanley Matthews, the great soccer star, represented the 50s; and Denis Compton was their sportsman of the 40s. I know nothing about cricket, except that England often lose Test matches, but I know Denis was a great player. What I didn't know, though, was that he played Test cricket for England before the war in the 1930s, yet was still good enough at football to play in a Cup Final for my team Arsenal in 1950 – twenty years before I was born. He must have been pretty special. To be considered to be in that sort of company was very flattering, and we had a wonderful evening.

We met up with Lester and had dinner. We met Gary Lineker and his wife and they seemed very nice. Jimmy Hill was doing the introductions and we were all asked a couple of questions. I was asked: 'What was your best day in racing?' and 'Who is your sporting hero outside your own sport?' I cheated really, saying, 'Because I'm very young, the only sport I know much about is racing. In racing, my hero is Lester Piggott.' Everyone cheered and Lester smiled. They went round to everyone and when it came to Lester's turn, nobody would have expected his answer. I'm sure I didn't. Lester is sixty years old now and you'd have thought that there were any number of people from when he was younger that he could have mentioned. But he said 'Damon Hill', a great compliment to Damon, and it also shows that Lester's a frustrated racing driver. Certainly, people who've been driven by him would think that! Anyway, it was a great night, and we ended up for the first time in my life at Annabel's night club. It looked a very nice place, but it was a Tuesday and we were the only people there. The next day I was back home in Newmarket to work with the Channel Four television people at the July meeting, one of the highlights of the year in English racing. The July course is very informal, the weather's always great and the racing is of a very high standard. The meeting is often chosen by the top stables to give their promising two-year-olds their first race – Alhaarth and Mark Of Esteem were first and second in a maiden there in the 1995 July meeting – and the Group 1 July Cup, on the Thursday, is one of the most important sprints of the entire season. One horse I would soon be riding which ran that week was David Loder's Bahamian Bounty. He, like Mark Of Esteem the year before, was not quite ready to win first time out, but within a few weeks I would be delighted to get the mount on him, with good reason.

By now I was having some regular physiotherapy, but, once the July meeting was finished, I didn't really want to stay around doing nothing, seeing horses I would have ridden win for others. So I saw John and said, 'I'm going to Sardinia. There's no point staying around and getting frustrated. I'll be able to do some more swimming in the sea and get some sun – it will be good for my arm.' Before we left I went to the local sports shop and bought a couple of light wrist-weights, just half a kilo each, and some springs to squeeze in my hand. We stayed at the family's house in Sardinia where I'd spent all those summers when I was a little boy. Dad was from there, and, apart from Milan, where he worked, it was my original home, so I felt very comfortable. Every day I would go into the sea. Where they live is on a bay and to swim across it's probably half a mile, and I would swim across. Then I'd relax in the afternoons in the sunshine. Catherine was great at that time. You need support when you are trying to overcome something like a major injury and she was always there. I wore the weights on my wrist and we would walk the beach. It was almost three miles there and back. While I walked, I'd move my arms up and down. I'd straighten my arm and then pull it up to the shoulder. I found that easy, but to put the hand behind my back and then attempt to lift the weights was much more painful. It really hurt the muscle at the back of the arm.

I would do that exercise at least one hundred times as I walked along the beach. It was painful, but I got to accept the pain as I realised that if I wanted to proceed I'd have to pay a price. If you do nothing, the muscle will not build up again. I wasn't going mad – there was only one pound on each wrist – but I could feel the benefit each day. By the end of the week I was doing the exercise two hundred times a day. By now my arm was around ninety per cent straight and I could touch my shoulder with no problems. I had planned to stay for ten days but because I was already feeling ready to start riding horses again, I cut the trip short by four days. I said to myself, 'You've done as much as you can with the weights and the swimming. Now it's time to get on the gee-gees.' We flew back that Thursday, and on Friday 25 July, I went to see John to show him my arm. He couldn't believe it.

I told him I'd like to give it a go the following Monday and ride out for the first time. That weekend, to prepare myself, I began a regular exercise programme in the gym at the Bedford Lodge. I started with forty lengths of the swimming pool, went on to pull a few weights (around five kilos), and then went on to the rowing machine. The hardest thing I tried at that stage was to push myself against the wall, when the arm felt quite sore.

The next Monday I went in early and John put me on a horse for the first time. As ever, he was considerate, and selected a great favourite in the yard, a horse nicknamed The Tortoise, which is a bit unkind, as he's won a couple of races, but he is pretty slow. It's probably best not to reveal his real name as his owner might not be too amused by the nickname. He's just the sort you'd expect him to be with that name, a lovely, quiet, easy ride, and for my first ride on Monday 29 July, I just went gently up the hill with him. On the Tuesday, I did a couple of canters, again with no ill effects and then the next day, the second day of the Goodwood summer meeting, I agreed with Julian Wilson to ride out at Lady Herries's stables, a few miles from the beautiful course up in the Sussex Downs. Julian was organising some filming which would be shown during the BBC coverage of the Goodwood meeting, another of the big highlights I would be missing. At least, by now, I could see some light at the end of my tunnel!

On the surface, my day at Angmering Park was fine, and

it all looked okay on the television screen. I rode Harbour Dues, who at the time was a short-priced ante-post favourite for the Tote-Ebor, the big handicap at the York August meeting. They told me Harbour Dues was a nice quiet ride, and he actually was, but for me the day was a disaster. After I got on the horse, my arm began to get really painful. After the first two days back on a horse, my hopes had been high, but all it took was one day with the pain again for me to lose confidence once more.

So, after Goodwood, I had to get back and increase the work in the gym. I was still riding out every morning for John and then I'd go down to the gym in the afternoons. Now it was a full hour and a half each day, starting with a forty-length swim, followed by the weights, a jog on the running machine for about one and a half miles, then a row on the rowing machine, and ending with fifty press-ups.

At this point, I was also having plenty of physiotherapy. Liz Minter, who was once married to Alan Minter, the former world professional boxing champion, now operates as a masseuse in Newmarket. I've known her for years, and she's great. She would work my arm so hard, it really helped me, and helped the arm relax. Liz is busy, so was not always available, but, by luck, I came across another physio, Mike Rogers, who'd been in charge of physiotherapy at Glasgow Rangers and some other big football clubs. He's nearly retired now, but he's still brilliant at the job. While he works, he's got a thousand stories about a lot of the footballers and what they used to get up to. Some of it made me blush! The hard work in the gym, Liz's and Mike's efforts and also a little extra assistance from an ultrasound machine, operated on me by Fiona and Rose, the girls at the Grosvenor House Clinic in Newmarket, meant that I soon felt ready. It was midweek in the first week of August and I felt really good. I said, 'I want to give it a go.' We agreed on a low-pressure evening meeting at Newmarket on the Friday night and a ride on a nice quiet two-year-old. I was back. Had I ever been away?

10 The Comeback

The horse I was to ride for my comeback was a backward youngster called Conon Falls, who would need an education and not too much hard riding from his unfit jockey in his first race. I'd had a sit on Conon Falls a few mornings before the race and he'd seemed a good, sensible horse to ride. On the morning of Friday 9 August 1996, looking forward to the comeback, I was very excited, and as I made the short drive to the track late that afternoon, I was very nervous, very excited. It was funny, but as I arrived in the weighing room I noticed everyone else's faces looking worn out. The other jockeys had been going through their summer agony, with their long days and evening meetings. As for me, while a little worried, I felt as fresh as a daisy, too fresh really, and I seemed to be jumping around everywhere. It must have irritated some of the jockeys, but they gave me a great welcome, and so did the crowd that night.

The race went fine for me, and though Conon Falls only

finished in the middle, we weren't expecting much more and the delicate first venture for both of us was safely achieved. Even an hour after the race I was still very excited and hyped up, as though I'd won a big race. I decided to take Catherine to the Hole in the Wall restaurant, just outside Newmarket. The food was excellent as usual, but all of a sudden I felt so tired. The adrenalin, which must have been pumping hard all day to keep me going, suddenly stopped. We went home and I was in bed by nine – exhausted. Luckily for me, the next afternoon's races were again at Newmarket. I had three rides, not expecting too much of any of them, and my expectations proved correct. Three unplaced horses.

At this time of year, top jockeys spend most Sundays travelling to race on the Continent, and that weekend, there was the choice of riding in Deauville or at Leopardstown in Ireland. David Loder had planned to run a nice two-year-old called Bahamian Bounty in the Heinz 57 Phoenix Stakes, a Group 1 race in Ireland, and the day before my comeback ride at Newmarket I had agreed to take the ride. Then David called the next day and told Matty that he would wait another week and run the horse in France. John had been happy for me to ride David's horse as he had Leap Of Joy in a Group 3 race the same day in Leopardstown, so once David's horse came out, I still flew across, but just for the one ride. Leap Of Joy didn't have much luck in running and finished third. So far, the comeback was not looking too good.

Next stop, on Monday, Windsor. During the summer, if it's Monday it has to be Windsor, and usually at night, but by the middle of August, as the days are getting ever shorter, we get a couple of afternoon meetings there. Windsor that day was the scene of another much-publicised comeback:

Walter Swinburn's return six months after his terrible fall in Hong Kong was even more momentous for him than my own comeback had been for me. Okay, I got hurt when Shawanni fell on me at Newbury, but when Walter crashed through the rails at Sha Tin back in February, for several days they thought he might die from his severe head injuries. His comeback to full health, starting in intensive care thousands of miles from home, was, literally, painfully slow and in the last few weeks, it was also frustrating as he had to accept a delayed return because of a technicality.

The race in which Walter was looking for a winning start on Talathath, a four-year-old horse trained at Newmarket by Chris Dwyer, was a handicap over one mile and I also had a ride, in my case on an old friend, the eleven-year-old Cape Pigeon. It was nice for Walter that an above-average crowd at Windsor gave him a great welcome, and there were plenty of TV cameras that day to see his comeback. We were all happy to see him back.

As I said, Cape Pigeon is a really nice horse and over the years I've ridden him quite a lot. He'd won a claiming race at Windsor very easily a little earlier in the season, and it's in that class that he is most likely to win. I usually end up riding him two or three times a year and I think I've won on him twice in selling or claiming races. He and another horse went off like scalded cats and I couldn't get him into the lead on his own for a couple of furlongs. I admit in hindsight I went too fast for the old boy and left nothing for the end of the race.

Meanwhile, Walter was coming to challenge and when I saw him I gave my horse a couple of back-handers. The poor old boy was knackered, and a furlong out Walter's horse went by and never looked in any danger. Because I burnt Cape Pigeon out in the early part of the race, he was very tired. So out of consideration for him – after all, he's an eleven-year-old – I just pushed him out to the line, before which Tony McGlone's horse caught and beat us by a short head for second. Perhaps in the eyes of some sections of the public, my riding at the end of the race did not look very good, but what they should have looked at to understand what I did was the entire race. If I did anything wrong – and underneath it there seemed to be the suggestion that I and maybe the other jockeys allowed Walter to win – it was merely that I went too fast at the beginning. When Cape Pigeon got tired, I thought it better not to hit him when he may then have weakened even more.

The stewards called me in to explain my riding. I did, and they accepted my explanation, which I think was the correct thing to do. They know I'm not a butcher and the poor old fellow, after all, is eleven years old and gives you everything on the bridle anyway. So, while Walter had his first win after his return at the first time of asking, I'd been riding four days without any luck. My next chance was to be at Salisbury on Wednesday, when John was running a nice filly called Altamura in a Listed race. It wasn't until after she had run a very good race to win the Upavon Stakes that day that I heard about a letter which Mr Eric Gadsden, who owns Cape Pigeon, had written to the newspapers. It said that I hadn't ridden to his orders, that the horse should have won, that it was disgusting that the stewards had done nothing about it, and that I was a disgrace, suggesting that we were all riding for Walter and not for our owners and trainers. He ended by saying that he would be selling all his horses – I think he owned one other apart from Cape Pigeon – and would not be buying any more – because of me.

Naturally I was very sad to hear about this and, like the

controversy after the 2,000 Guineas, in a way it spoiled my comeback winner. In the end, it took me almost a week to get over that particular upset, and it took a lot of the satisfaction from the fact that my first win had been in an important race for my boss. The next morning, as usual, the newspapers were all still talking about the Cape Pigeon incident – as far as I'm concerned there wasn't one anyway – and not my winner. It was a bit different for Walter. In his case they were all delighted for him and concentrated on his win. The thing that disappointed me most was the fact that here was an owner, still running an old horse and getting pleasure from him, but, reading his letter, it seemed to me he actually wanted his loyal old horse to be beaten up. I wrote him a couple of lines, saying I was sorry he thought that way. In my mind, I wanted that to finish the matter, but a week later Mr Gadsden was still making comments to the papers, and, astonishingly, those comments were still being printed.

The hardest part of anything is achieving the first milestone. It had taken almost a week to get my first winner, but within another ten days it all seemed like I'd never been away, and the winners kept clicking, as though I'd hardly missed anything. Before the flood of winners, though, there was a less than successful afternoon in Deauville, my first visit there of the year, when I would normally have made a number of day trips across for the top races at the picturesque track. The French really know how to relax in August and the jockeys also take their chance to mix business with plenty of pleasure. The life is comfortable, the races valuable, and the weather normally beautiful. We had two Godolphin horses entered on the Thursday, with Charnwood Forest our main runner in the Prix Jacques Le Marois, a Group 1 race over a mile, which is probably the highlight of the entire Deauville meeting in terms of quality. I had been very disappointed to miss the ride on Charnwood Forest when he'd won the Queen Anne Stakes, the opening race of Royal Ascot; he'd been the first horse to ram home to me what I was going to be denied in my enforced absence. He had been beaten since in the Sussex Stakes, by First Island, but I was going to have my chance of revenge for Godolphin against First Island in the Juddmonte International at York the following week. Now, though, this was my first really important ride. We'd also taken Wall Street, a decent three-year-old for a supporting race. Both horses finished fourth and by this time I was getting a bit grumpy because the winners weren't coming.

While I was flying home, Catherine got a call from John asking her to tell me, 'Just ride by instinct. You're thinking too much and trying too hard. Just go out and ride.' It was good advice, especially as, next day, Friday, would be my first visit back to Newbury where, just nine weeks before, the accident had occurred. As soon as I arrived there I had to admit it felt strange. Going into the paddock for the first race, it all came back again, and when I got on Catechism, the filly of John's I was riding in the two-year-old maiden race, I recalled the fall and decided to take my feet out of the irons, just in case. Perhaps you could accuse me of being over-cautious and by the end of the day I would have had to agree with you, as by then we were really rolling.

Catechism had raced twice already and finished second each time, but, with a few more fancied newcomers in a big field, I thought maybe a place would come our way. If your luck is out, you won't get a run, but this was going to be my day and, sure enough, the split came at exactly the right time. Catechism went through it and went on to win, when ninety-nine times out of 100 you wouldn't get the split from that position. My next ride was also for John, in a valuable three-year-old handicap over ten furlongs. I was on Greenstead, a horse who had won a maiden at Newmarket's big three-day July meeting. The bookies weren't too interested, and he started at 13–2, but won like an odds-on shot. Again we got the gap when we needed it and, by that time, confidence was really starting to go through my veins.

The big race of the day was the Hungerford Stakes, an important seven-furlong Group 3 race, and I was riding Bin Rosie, a bit of a character but a talented one, for David Loder's stable. David fancied his chances as Bin Rosie had been over to France and won a Listed race. He thought that the pace was sure to be fast with Green Perfume, a confirmed front-runner, in the field, and so it proved. For the third time, I got my gap when I wanted it, and again my horse ran all the way to the line. Three winners in a day on the track where I'd been hurt. John had said 'Ride by instinct' and it had worked. In one day my confidence was suddenly back. You can see how some jockeys, unlucky enough to have to live on three rides a day, find their confidence going when they get on a long losing run. When I'm busy, when the evening meetings come along, a run of thirty consecutive losers may mean as little as only three days without a winner. For me, though, having been off for eight weeks, it was especially important that the fears and worries that might have developed during my absence were quickly overcome. John was right, until Friday I was a little bit nervous, thinking too much and trying too hard.

I felt much more comfortable going to the track on the second day of the meeting. I rode Head Over Heels, a nice filly owned by John's wife Rachel. John was really keen for her to win and get the valuable black type a Listed win would entitle her to. For a filly, to get 'black type' is most important. When fillies and mares are sold, they are listed in catalogues printed by the respective bloodstock sales companies around the world. Keeneland in Kentucky, Tattersalls at Newmarket, Goff's at Kildare in Ireland and Deauville in France stage the major sales and that is where the 'black type' fillies are likely to appear, either to be sold, or in the pedigrees of other horses, most importantly, yearlings who are in their families. Black type means winning or being placed in either Group or Listed races, and when a filly achieves black type it is great news for her owner. As I said, John was keen for her to win, and actually gave me the riding instructions a week before the race. As instructed, I always had her close behind the leaders on the rails, again got a gap when I pulled her out to tackle Olympic Spirit, and got up on the line to win by a short head.

The day's main race was the Geoffrey Freer Stakes, over a mile and five furlongs, and my mount was the Queen's filly, Phantom Gold, who was making her last appearance as she is already in foal to the successful stallion Cadeaux Généreux. Like any expectant mother, an in-foal mare can feel very energetic for some time in the early part of her pregnancy. Many fillies do well when in foal, and Phantom Gold certainly showed her best form here. Lord Huntingdon, who trains her, had not been enjoying a great season, and neither had the Queen's horses been in brilliant form, but I was hopeful, as the only previous time I had ridden Phantom Gold had been in the 1995 Ribblesdale Stakes at Royal Ascot, which she'd won. This final race was meticulously and carefully planned by Lord Huntingdon and Lord Carnarvon, the Queen's racing manager, who is also Chairman of Newbury racecourse. They decided to run Whitechapel, a good stayer also owned by Her Majesty, to ensure the good pace needed for Phantom Gold to show her best form. The plan worked well, especially as Whitechapel found a friend, Reg Akehurst's Wayne County, to share the work.

Meanwhile, I sat at the back and took my time. The filly is a little tricky, as she needs to be settled, but when she comes through and gets in a challenging position she tends to be a little one-paced, and, when she hits the front, she tends to pull up. So, with her, timing is everything. You try to get her running, and get up there and then try not to allow her to stop when she does make her move. Crucially, it all worked out right because of Whitechapel, whose strong pace helped me time everything to perfection. It's always a thrill to ride for the Queen. I've been lucky riding her horses, and when I pulled up I remember thinking, 'I hope she was watching this on TV at Balmoral', where she has her summer holiday. I'm sure she was.

So we left Newbury on the Saturday night, with five wins to show for my first two days back at the track where I'd been badly hurt such a short time before. It was as if I'd never been away from riding, and with a Listed winner at Salisbury, a Group 3 at Newbury, and another Listed and a Group 2 on the second day at Newbury, I had to be delighted. Some jockeys would be delighted with that haul in a career. I'd been lucky enough to get it within three riding days in England.

I wasn't expecting too much as we set off for Deauville on the Sunday. The Prix Morny, over six furlongs, is the first leg of France's three top races for two-year-olds. All Group 1, they comprise of the Morny, over six, the Prix de la Salamandre at Longchamp, over seven, and the Grand Critérium, over a mile at the Prix de l'Arc de Triomphe meeting. Some top French-trained horses have won all three to become France's and Europe's unchallenged champion two-year-old, and as I set off with David Loder to ride Bahamian Bounty nobody gave us much chance of beating France's latest star Zamindar. David had switched his colt from his planned race in Ireland the previous week-end, and I wasn't unhappy with this, as the extra week had given me the chance to ride myself into form. But we knew Bahamian Bounty, who had made a promising start when second at Newmarket and then won well in modest class at Yarmouth, was trying to climb a mountain against the horse I called 'Baby Zafonic'. Zafonic was the horse which in 1992 dominated the two-year-olds in Europe, but instead of trying for the Grand Critérium, he came to England and easily won the Dewhurst Stakes. The next season, he won the 2,000 Guineas at Newmarket in brilliant style and while he then raced only once more (unsuccessfully) before retiring, he still has a great reputation. His first crop of yearlings were presented for sale in the autumn of 1996. Zamindar, like Zafonic, is owned and was bred by Prince Khalid Abdulla and trained by André Fabre, France's leading trainer.

The word from France was that 'Baby Zafonic' was 'as good as his brother', and 'a world beater' but David and Edward St George, who owns Bahamian Bounty, reckoned that if nothing took him on, no one would know how good he was. In the race, I tracked Thierry Jarnet, who was riding the favourite, a heavily-backed 5–1 on shot. Just before the furlong marker, I pounced and went by him, and although Zamindar kept after us, we won by a short neck. As I came back, I was dying to do my Angel Cordero leap again, even though I had resolved never to repeat it after all the hassle following the 2,000 Guineas. I reasoned that the French are not as fussy as can be the case in England, so I did the leap, and as usual the crowd seemed to enjoy it. Happily for me,

I didn't land on my elbow, like the last time I took an unorthodox exit from a horse!

When a champion is dethroned, the tendency, I'm afraid, especially from the pressmen who have been hyping him, is to look for something or someone to blame. It was like that in the 2,000 Guineas when they said the watering was uneven and Mark Of Esteem was a lucky winner because of it. There had to be a fall guy for Zamindar's defeat and this time it was the jockey. Mr Fabre and, I think, also Prince Khalid felt that Thierry Jarnet had been caught out by my manoeuvre. Certainly, once we went ahead there wasn't too much time for Thierry to get back, but I thought my horse idled when he hit the front and was probably value for a little more than a short neck. I saw the race myself from the perfect place, in the front seat, and I don't think Thierry did anything wrong. Maybe his horse will still become the star they thought. I know it hurt the Prince, because at York when I bumped into him after the Juddmonte International, which he so generously sponsors, he said, 'You didn't beat my horse, you beat my jockey.' I disagree, politely, I hope, with his opinion, but agree that what happens when horses meet on an individual day need not happen when they meet again. On that day, though, I believe most people did not give enough credit to my horse. It was nice to see David Loder coming back to form as his horses had been under a cloud for much of the summer. He was one of the guys who backed me when I most needed it, and I rate him very highly as a trainer. His misfortunes of the summer, when his horses were wrong, showed that, like everyone else, when things go wrong you just have to wait for them to come right again. If you have the talent, as David does, the success will come when the horses are back in good health. Getting back with a Group 1 winner so soon after Bin Rosie's good win at Newbury was, with some other important races coming up at York, the boost he needed.

11 The Race of the Year

Funnily enough, although I'd been in a good run, from the Saturday night before I left for France until Monday, when my horses did nothing, I was in a bad mood, as Catherine kept reminding me. I was tense, all right, and for a good reason: on Tuesday I would be back on one of my favourite horses and one of the biggest stars in European racing. I'd missed Halling's repeat win in the Coral-Eclipse Stakes at Sandown during my injury, but I'd won the Prix Ganay in France on him before my accident when he'd told me that he'd not been affected by those two defeats by Cigar on dirt. Now, though, was the real test. That Monday night, Catherine and I sat in the front room sulking to each other. Trying to put me in a better mood, she said, 'Don't worry, he's a certainty. He can't get beat.' I wasn't so sure, and in some cases I think it's good to take a negative view, believing a horse like Halling can get beat, so at least you pay more attention to all the possibilities. So I was looking at the

163

field and thinking, 'If I make the running, would that help First Island (the horse that beat Charnwood Forest at Goodwood)? If the pace of the race is too slow, would that give the advantage to Bijou d'Inde, who has the turn of foot of a top miler?' I thought it all through, and was determined to get the tactics right, especially as this was one of the most important races I'd not won, and one that my dad had won on Wollow more than twenty years earlier.

When I ride for Godolphin, however important the race, I am given plenty of freedom on how to ride each horse. The Godolphin team sits down and debates and carefully plans the race. I decide I will try to do this and follow plan A. If that is not working in the early stages, then I'll go to plan B, C or D. I'm very lucky to have that freedom and that was reassuring for me when I went out for the ride on Halling. It was probably the race of the year, contested by five Group 1 winners. There was a lot of tension as we stood in the paddock beforehand, with Sheikh Mohammed and all the entourage, and there was a lot of discussion between them about how the race might go. They were all tense, and understandably, as no horse had ever achieved the feat of winning two Coral-Eclipse Stakes and two Juddmonte Internationals. I was tense, like them, but just to make myself feel a little more at ease, while I was standing there, Halling walked past, and I turned to Sheikh Mohammed, pointed to Halling and said: 'Is he any good?' He didn't answer, but I think it eased the pressure a little bit.

Halling cantered beautifully to the start, and felt great as usual. All the jockeys were concentrating hard on what they were doing, and, in a race like the Juddmonte International, each of the horses has a stalls handler allocated to him. There's an old guy in the north, called Sid, but whom we know as 'Vicious' because of the ill-fated member of the Sex Pistols group – they were before my time, of course. Vicious was looking after me, and as he came to greet me and check the horse's girth, I was thinking: 'I'm going out there and doing what I have to do.' I saw him coming over to me and said, 'Hi, Vicious, how are you?' He said, 'Guess what happened to me last week? My son, aged twenty-two, hanged himself.' I thought, 'Jesus Christ. Here I am worrying about a horse race and here's a man who's lost his son and still doing his job.' It helped put everything in perspective. Vicious was just going through the motions, really. I felt really sad, but, as you do, when we went into the stalls, I forgot all about it and waited for the gates to open.

As I waited, my one worry was that I was drawn near the rails. I wanted to make it, but if Halling was to miss the break and not get to the front I would have to switch to plan B. He didn't have to lead necessarily, just get a nice break. The stalls opened and Halling jumped off well and was quickly into his stride. The only thing going through my mind at that stage was that the pace needed to be even. That way there would be no advantage or disadvantage. That would suit me fine and I knew my horse was better than the others. 'They can't beat me,' I thought. You feel how comfortable he is and go at that speed. Not every horse is the same, and I quickened the pace entering the straight where I had a very nice rhythm.

He's an amazing horse. When John trained him to win the Cambridgeshire as a three-year-old, before he first went to Dubai and into the care of Godolphin at the end of 1994, he was very immature and had no gears. That's not quite right. He probably had them, but didn't know how to use them. As a five-year-old he is almost certainly an even better horse than he was at four.

When we came into the straight, I brought him to the middle of the track. He prefers to run right-handed and to have a rail to run down on his right-hand side. York, of course, is a left-handed track and by taking him out to the middle there would be less danger that he would hang right away from the rail on his left. If he were to do that when another horse came up alongside to challenge, the problem would be that he could interfere with them and lose the race in the stewards' room. I thought it was common sense, and the going in the middle of the track seemed just as fast. I'd given him a little breather before the straight, and now took a quick look under my legs at the other horses. I saw they were all in Indian file, and playing my game. It was time to stretch them as we got to the three-furlong pole.

Halling is a very intelligent horse and to make him go faster all I need to do is lean forward a little and he accelerates for me. You lean forward and he goes lower like a cheetah as it sprints. From going along evenly, he gets down. I asked for a gear but without asking for everything. After all, were was still two and a half furlongs to run. Then just before the furlong pole, I had a look, and then asked him again, and he found another gear and drew away to win by three and a half lengths. You have a good horse if he can quicken once. To do that is an achievement. To quicken twice, that's exceptional, and the mark of a true champion. Like Halling.

Coming back to the winner's enclosure I felt great. It was probably the performance of the year in one of the best races of the entire season. All the people had come to York to greet a great champion – Halling – and I was part of it. He'd more than fulfilled every expectation. I felt the crowd wanted me to do something. I punched the air a couple of times and got a great response from them. As we reached the winner's enclosure all the owners and their friends were there with big smiles on their faces and they were hugging each other in pure excitement at what they'd seen. I'd vowed never to do my Angel Cordero jump again in England, but the atmosphere overruled any such negative thought. I said to myself: 'What the heck?' There's a right time for everything in life. There's a right time to jump. I knew the horse would not worry about it, because he told me! It's a great feeling. I'll probably never get a welcome from a crowd at any time in my career like the one the enthusiastic Yorkshire people gave me that day. So I made the most of it. I was worried for a minute that Sheikh Mohammed and his elder brother Sheikh Maktoum would not like it, and I must confess that since the Guineas I had regretted my actions that day, having gone too far on that occasion, especially as I hadn't got back to the winner's circle. But their faces told me it was all right. I wasn't quite so sure about the stewards though. Funnily enough, as I jumped I just caught a glimpse of another Yorkshireman out of the corner of my eye. That was Mark Tompkins, ironically, going out with his saddle before running Even Top in the following race, the Great Voltigeur Stakes. I thought I saw his lips move, but it was too fleeting a glimpse. I suppose he was saying 'Silly booger' in his best Yorkshire accent. But then I reckon I might be forgiven by now for what he called being unprofessional, as I see he now has a horse running from his stable which he has called 'Frankie' and says he's named it after me. Of course, Mark has to have the last word and says the horse is not as silly as me!

After unsaddling and watching the presentation, I had a

lovely interview on Channel 4 TV with Brough Scott. They have an interview point at the entrance to the winner's circle and weighing room closest to the main stand where all the punters go, and there was a massive crowd on that side listening to us. I said that one of the most enjoyable things about racing at York was that the Yorkshire people all get so involved in the racing. They cheered me all the time, and every sentence seemed to bring another great cheer. As an Italian I now realise that Yorkshire people do not think that their country is part of England. They think that the rest of England is a small part of Yorkshire! The one disappointment, considering the race was so important, was that there was no memento for the jockey. You don't want anything valuable, but to have a little reminder for your old age that you won the Juddmonte International on the great Halling would be nice. Especially as my dad also won the race all those years ago.

The other main ride for me that day was Mons, who ran well in the Great Voltigeur, finishing second to Dushyantor. I'd tried to ride him like Halling, but that was unfair on him, and he did well as it turned out. Maybe I went a little too easily, as he was coming back again at the winner in the last half-furlong, but sometimes, when you ask a horse to go half a beat faster than is comfortable for him, he doesn't get home. That day he seemed a decent St Leger prospect to me.

The second day of the York Ebor meeting started with a double disappointment. The first setback was that Pricket, who would have been the assured favourite, had to miss the Yorkshire Oaks because of a minor problem. Luckily Godolphin had a decent deputy in Russian Snows, a filly which had been trained in Ireland by John Oxx as a three-year-old, but then went to Dubai for the winter. She'd run well in a race on the Nad Al Sheba track in February and although she hadn't run for six months, the team were hopeful of a good run and she started favourite. In the race, over a mile and a half, she was in a good position but when I tried to edge out to make her challenge at the two-furlong pole, I couldn't get out. Richard Quinn was on my outside and upsides and he had me boxed in. I couldn't do anything about it. Then Richard came off the bridle and started to lose ground on his filly, and gave me the sign to 'go on, take it'. I moved out a second too quickly and didn't allow him quite enough time to drop out. I brushed his filly and it didn't make any difference to Whitewater Affair, his mount, but it looked from the head-on camera that I'd barged my way out. That was the stewards' view and they banned me for four days for 'irresponsible riding'. I was upset by the decision, especially as it meant that because of my two earlier bans, in April and May, each of two days, I was getting close to the mandatory extra two weeks ban once a jockey gets twelve days in total under the same heading. I don't like the rule, which is a new one. I believe the jockeys have been doing their best to keep within the rules, but they are riding under a system which does not apply in any of the other countries. The thought of two extra weeks after all my missed racing during the year was a great worry coming to the other big races at York. The jockeys' representatives on the Jockeys' Association are keen to get a different system into operation. No one wants to see top jockeys banned for weeks at a time for marginal interference. The penalty, to my mind, is far out of proportion to the crime. It's a bit like having penalty points on a driving licence. The idea probably looked good in the first place, but in practice it's like having a gun to your head for a whole year.

I didn't have too long to dwell on this suspension, though, before I was back in action on another of David Loder's nice two-year-olds. I'd ridden Abou Zouz when he'd made a most impressive winning début at the Guineas meeting back in the spring. That day we'd thought he was pretty special, but then he'd run very disappointingly at Kempton and that was probably the start of David's bad time. He was ridden by John Reid that day and the horse was never happy, he was very sweaty and upset. He ran a terrible race for no reason at all it seemed and it puzzled all of us. Then, two weeks before York, Abou Zouz started to show his old sparkle again. For me and David it was third time lucky in the race. In David's first season, in 1993, Fast Eddy had finished a very good third behind First Island and Mister Baileys. The following year, I'd thought Fallow, owned by Sheikh Mohammed, had the race in his pocket when Chilli Billy came out of the clouds to win going away. This time, though, there was no mistake. I had Abou Zouz well there on the outside all the way. We hit the front with one hundred yards to go, and although he swerved a little to his left, he had a bit in hand. David, like me, was on fire, winning a Group 3, a Group 1 and then a Group 2 within five days. It showed how in racing just a week can change someone's life. In the previous three months, while his horses were wrong, he was starting to question whether he was still a good trainer. Just like for me, that was not the end of David's York story.

After the second day, Wednesday, at York, Catherine and I stayed up for the night, and it was a nice change to have an easy time. We had a very pleasant early dinner, but I was really tired and went to bed very early. I woke up and as the hotel was so close to the track – it is just at the end of the straight course – I decided to go to the weighing room to see how my weight was. So I left at nine thirty, and Catherine, who had been racing on the Wednesday, when she'd spent the day in the company of Johnny Murtagh's wife Orla, decided to have a day in town shopping and sight-seeing, as the Murtaghs had gone back to Ireland on Wednesday night. I was going to have to do 8st 6lb on one of John's horses, North Song, which is owned by Rachel, and because I wanted to do the best I could on him – he was running in a valuable handicap – did not want to put up any over-weight. So, after discovering I needed to lose just over a pound, I took a very steady run, really a light jog, around the track. I went from the weighing room down to the mile and a quarter start and then back around the course, about two miles in all, but very steady. Afterwards, I sat outside the weighing room in the sunshine, as I had been sweating and wanted to dry off while I read the papers. I weighed myself again and found I'd lost around one pound already, but so that I could be able to use a chamois on North Song – it's not something John's fussy about, but it's more comfortable for the horse to have a soaked chamois leather under the saddle when he runs – I needed to lose a bit more.

The chamois weighs about half a pound, so I decided on half an hour in the sauna. After the sauna, I was about 8st 3.5lb stripped, comfortably light enough to do the weight on North Song. I was doubly keen to take every advantage. As well as doing my best on John's horse, there was the matter of the London Clubs Charity Trophy, which goes to the jockey who rides the most winners at the big meetings. I knew that Pat Eddery was going to be a threat as we were on the same number of wins going into the final day, and in the event of equal winners the biggest number of seconds decides it. It was still early, so I took the chance to grab a short sleep in the ambulance room and then began to prepare for my full book of rides.

Looking at my rides, I reckoned I had a great chance, especially as the day was beginning for me with another of David's good two-year-olds. I had ridden Indiscreet in a gallop the previous week and on what we'd seen that day we all thought a lot of him. The one thing we weren't sure of was whether when he was asked to lengthen he would be able to do so. The race was the Convivial Maiden, always one of the hottest two-year-old maiden races of the year, and the race in which such great racehorses as Danehill, In The Groove and Owington had got their winning ways going. I doubt if any of them was more impressive than Indiscreet, a colt from the first crop of St Jovite (one of the best mile and a half horses of the past decade, when you consider he won the Irish Derby by twelve lengths and the King George by six).

All the papers were saying Indiscreet would need more than six furlongs and his breeding certainly said the same thing. No one told Indiscreet though and we were always going really sweetly on the outside. There were three or four others, all from stables with good lines to two-year-old form, who were reportedly well fancied, but Indiscreet simply blew them out of the water. I did my lean forward when Willie Carson started to work on the favourite and we went clear in a few strides. Imagine my shock then that he broke the two-year-old track record, first time out, without me ever having to get after him. He shocked everyone, including me. I knew he was nice and I love the way he tries to give everything to you. That made it three for the meeting and another winner on the way to the Trophy.

If we weren't sure how good the track record was that Indiscreet had set, we didn't have long to wait to find out. David ran Bianca Nera, a filly that had won her only race just a week before at Beverley, a track where we've had a lot of success together. He didn't decide to run at York before I'd already accepted the ride on a filly of Michael Stoute's and for most of the week David was pestering me to see if I would become available. I rode Moonshine Girl for Michael and she's a nice filly, keen to please. In the race she was a bit buzzy, which can often happen with a filly there because the York track is so open. She pulled a bit and didn't feel right and later we found she'd been struck into. I was disappointed, and especially as I could have ridden the winner. Bianca Nera won in really determined style. The Lowther is a Group 2 race and is always hard to win and I was pleased in one way for David, but disappointed for myself. Bianca Nera saw off several challenges in the last furlong and had a much harder race than Indiscreet, so the fact that she took a second longer to run the same distance put the colt's great first run into perspective.

I was back with David on his sprinter Struggler for the third race, the Nunthorpe Stakes, one of the biggest sprint races of the entire year, and the most important five-furlong race in England. This was the race that gave Sir Mark Prescott his first ever win in a Group 1 race after many years' trying. Pivotal was the horse who came late and fast to win from Eveningperformance.

Before the race, it was beginning to get hot and I started sweating freely. I'd not taken any drinks because I was doing light later on, just a sip of Coca Cola. Struggler was fine going to the start. David told me he had been missing the break lately – he was left in the stalls at Royal Ascot – and told me to watch for that. Unfortunately, he jumped too good, pulled for three furlongs when I was hoping to be covered up behind the leaders. Struggler is usually strong in five-furlong races, but this time after taking me along for three and a half furlongs, he died on the bridle and finished unplaced.

At York, when you finish in the first four you unsaddle right in front of the weighing room. When you are unplaced it's quite a walk back from the paddock, and I was trudging back when I bumped into John. 'Hurry up,' he said, 'I've got two to saddle.' That meant he wanted me to go straight into the jockeys' room, change into his horse's silks, change the weights in the saddle cloth and be ready to give the saddle back to him as soon as possible. I kinda snapped at him a little bit. Obviously, the heat and the thought of not being able to have a drink or any food all day was getting to me and I was a bit tetchy. I went straight into the room, got my light saddle out, changed and weighed out. I was 8st 6lb with a chamois. No bother! I gave the saddle to John and I could hardly believe it when he said: 'Come straight out, he's going down early.' So, instead of having a few minutes' rest, I had to go and put my hat on and then was out in a minute.

It was getting hotter all the time. There were plenty of runners in the race, so we went down really early and North Song was great, no trouble at all going to the start. Unfortunately, when I got there we had at least ten minutes to wait, so I got off and then had to keep leading him round so he wouldn't stiffen up. So there I was out in the sun for what seemed an unnecessary length of time. He's not the easiest of horses at the walk and, as we were walking, he was dragging me around, all the time sapping a little more of my strength. Eventually, the others came down and, when they started, North Song jumped off well. I decided to let him make the running and he was in a nice easy lead. When we turned for home, I came out to the middle of the track where I thought the ground was a little faster. A couple went by me a furlong or so out, but I saved a bit and they must have gone a bit early because North Song got back to beat them. Unfortunately, another horse came from way off the pace and came down the wide outside and we were second.

North Song had been fine in the race, but that wasn't the end of that particular story. The fun had not really started. When I went to pull him up, North Song bolted towards the stables. It was my fourth ride of the afternoon. I'd been leading him round for ten minutes under the hot sun and then pushing him all the way to the straight. Anyway, he wouldn't stop. Whatever I tried to do to stop him, he simply went faster and faster. By now his mouth was dead. I had no control, and we continued to head straight for the stables. We were still flat out and at the same time the starter was coming back in his car towards the finishing line and for a minute I thought my horse was going straight for the car and we were in for a spectacular collision. I wondered what I could do and thought: 'My God, my big accident!' I imagined the horse running into the car and maybe breaking his legs and whatever might happen to me. It had been just ten weeks since my major operation and it was at that point that my arm started to give – I didn't have any strength any more. Luckily, just when it seemed a crash was inevitable, he stopped all by himself. I took a deep breath, took him round and galloped him back. I was in a state. I was exhausted, my arms were aching, my hands burning having been rubbing on the reins in the heat, and I was sweating ever more. I was knackered. More importantly, I was also back late and, still grumpy, told John he'd given me a bad ride. It was not his fault, but obviously I was a little upset. I went into the jockeys' room. Again I was looking for a little recovery time before riding Daunt, another horse of John's, when John popped his head round the door and said, 'He's early too!' I tried to make it, but I was still late getting out and missed going down early. So John said, 'Ask to go down last, then.' Daunt is the biggest horse in John's stable, stands a full eighteen hands (six feet) high and is simply huge. Before going to the start, the horses trot down to the winning post from the paddock exit before cantering back. The York lead-up got to Daunt, however, and he was really buzzing. I tried to trot him across to the start, but couldn't hold him so I decided to get off halfway and walk the rest of the way to the start. Eventually, we were there, and once loaded, he jumped out and immediately started taking me on so much. When we came to the straight I started pushing, and did so all the way from the four-furlong pole to the winning post. We finished fifth. I went to stop him, and, like North Song, he didn't want to stop, but luckily this time I ran into the back of Jimmy Quinn, who'd finished just ahead of me in third. Jimmy was very nice to me and kinda towed me back. Lord Hartingdon, the owner, who was the first Chairman of the British Horse-Racing Board and is a very nice man, came to see his horse and on the spur of the moment I threw my saddle on the floor and said: 'You can't do this to me, John. Everything I ride today pulls.' Daunt had 9st 12lb and to carry the saddle back would have meant my carrying almost a couple of stones' dead weight. I was in no condition really to carry myself, let alone a heavy saddle the long way back to the weighing room. I told John: 'I'm knackered. I'm exhausted!' John kindly took pity on me and carried the saddle back for me.

I wanted to stop there and then and probably should have

done, but there was still the matter of the London Clubs Trophy. I should have won the Royal Ascot one this year, so I was anxious not to let this one slip away. North Song's second place added to my three winners meant that Pat couldn't beat me, but if Kevin Darley rode the last two winners, he'd sneak up on the rails. I was completely wiped out, but I felt that Annaba, one of the favourites for the Galtres Stakes, could help me clinch it. So I had a little excitement to help keep me going. I checked the weight, had a couple of minutes' rest and a glass of Coca-Cola before going out to the paddock once more. In the canter to the post, Annaba took me on. I couldn't believe it. Another horse pulling me all the way down to the start. In retrospect, I must have got to the stage where I could do nothing about it. Even a Jack Russell would have run away with me.

By now, I couldn't help making the running. I stayed out in front until three horses went by and I could do nothing about it. I was fighting to keep fourth for the whole of the last furlong and missed that, too. I'd pushed myself too far. When I pulled the filly up I couldn't get my breath back. I felt exhausted, gave the horse to her lad and simply sat down where I was. I took off the colours where I sat and was pouring with sweat. I told John I would have to give up my last ride, Forest Cat, a filly I'd done well on before, in the last race, and asked John to apologise to Julie Cecil, her trainer, and owner George Ward. I was taken to the ambulance room where they gave me Coca-Cola with sugar in an attempt to pump some energy into me. Then I had five cups of tea with lots of sugar, and rested there for forty-five minutes. While in there I saw Forest Cat finish third in the last race. Luckily, Kevin didn't win either race and thanks to North Song, who gave me one second place more than Pat,

I'd won the Trophy. I wasn't in the mood to collect it after the race so I flew straight back to Newmarket with John. On the way, I apologised to him for the day.

Re-thinking, I realised there is a difference between being fit and being fit to ride under duress. The time I'd had off meant that I needed a longer recovery time. After being unfit for more than two months, to go through such a severe schedule at the start of my comeback, culminating in three really busy days in York, drained my energies. I still thought my recovery rate was just as quick as before the accident, but I would have cause to reconsider that opinion very soon. On getting home, I thought, 'There's one remedy. Pasta and plenty of carbohydrate.' I ate a big plateful and went to bed. I had a good night's sleep and in the morning still felt a little under the weather, but I decided to go ahead and ride that day at Newmarket. I thought, 'Well, I've only got six easy rides at Newmarket.' It wasn't the case. After the third one, I felt like something had sucked all the strength out of me. The previous day's exertions had taken a lot more out of me than I'd thought. I took all the rides and kept going because I knew that I'd look a fool if I stopped halfway through the day. They would all have said, 'He had a bad day yesterday, he should have taken today off', and they would have been right. Luckily, all my rides were dream rides. Mick Channon, the former England footballer who is doing so well as a trainer, gave me two fantastic rides which took me through the race by themselves. After racing, I saw the doctor, who advised me to 'get some food into you'. I didn't want to miss the next day, when I would be renewing my association with another old friend – Mark Of Esteem, in the Tripleprint Mile at Goodwood.

12 Super Saturday

By the Friday night of my busy week at York I was beginning to worry. For the second day I'd felt very weak and when I saw the racecourse doctor at the end of the Newmarket meeting he asked whether I had been getting a good night's sleep. I told him I'd been a little edgy and he said it would be all right to take a sleeping tablet to help me relax. When I got back I called John and asked if I could take Saturday morning off. He was fine as usual and after having a nice salad I went to bed very early and took a sleeping pill. It must have worked because I slept through until nine the next morning and when I got up I felt much better than the previous day, properly rested and ready for another big day.

Today was going to be important for me and all the Godolphin people because, at Goodwood, Mark Of Esteem was having his first race since failing at Royal Ascot, and I was going to have my first ride on him since the 2,000

Guineas, which he'd won, but which had become a very controversial race for everything that had happened afterwards. He was one of a few nice rides I had scheduled that day at Goodwood and then later in the season's last evening meeting at Windsor. Peter Burrell, my business manager, had some time earlier arranged a day-long session with a video cameraman, who would come with us in Neil Foreman's plane, taking shots for a film which would be shown on airline magazine programmes and things like *Transworld Sport*, I think. It would be a 'day in the life' and the cameraman, a very nice man called Matt, could not have picked a better day to show me looking good!

As I looked through the papers before flying down to Goodwood from the July course at Newmarket, I thought, while I drank my coffee, that I had some good rides. Although Mark Of Esteem was the one to look forward to, and the most important as he was running in a Group 2 race, the Tripleprint Celebration Mile, I reckoned Sharaf Kabeer was my best chance of a winner. I'd ridden him at Kempton the day before the accident at Newbury and he'd won by miles. He was well beaten, when I was out of action, in the Irish Derby, but as I made a close study of his opponents in the Sport on Five race, which is a trial for the St Leger and run over a mile and three-quarters, I didn't think the opposition was very strong for a race of that type. I knew, judging on his win at Kempton, that the distance would be no problem and I fully expected him to win.

We got to the course at twelve-noon, having landed at Goodwood on the strip in the middle of the old car-racing track, which used to have Grand Prix races in the old days. Because I was so hopeful about Sharaf Kabeer, I told Matt that this should be the race to concentrate on with the filming, and as it was a little relaxed at the start of the day I sneaked him into the jockeys' room (not allowed, strictly speaking) for him to film me getting changed. I said, 'Build everything around that race.' I'm not sure whether Matt was a betting man, I reckon he might be, but after Sharaf Kabeer came home an easy three and a half length winner at the good price of 11–4, Matt had a stunned look on his face, which never really left it all day. This meant Godolphin would have another shot at the St Leger which we'd won the year before with Classic Cliché. Sharaf Kabeer was much less mature than Classic Cliché had been at this stage of his career, but he's a nice stayer with a good future, I'm certain of that.

Now we were ready for the big race. Mark Of Esteem had given us the biggest thrill of the year so far in the Guineas but he hadn't run well at Royal Ascot. At the back of my mind, there was a worry about him because of that, but I remembered that two weeks before Ascot he'd been meant to run in the Derby but had been ruled out because of a temperature. I think that was probably the main reason for his disappointing run, which clearly wasn't his form – much more logical than not liking the firm ground. He was beaten too far for it to be that. A week before Goodwood, Mark Of Esteem had a nice workout with me on the Limekilns gallop at Newmarket. One of my favourite phrases in racing, always used by over-excited stable lads when their horses work well, is that the horse is 'catching pigeons'. That day, Mark Of Esteem worked so brilliantly that after three furlongs he caught the pigeon, after five he cooked it, and, at the end of the seven-furlong gallop, he had indigestion!

On the work, then, he had to run well at Goodwood, but the Ascot defeat still played on my mind a bit, and I wondered whether he would be as good as on Guineas day. As with Halling in the Juddmonte International four days earlier, there was some tension in the paddock beforehand, and one worry for me was that I was drawn on the inside of the seven runners, right on the rail. I explained to Sheikh Mohammed that from that draw, the one thing I had to try to ensure was getting a run. Some tracks are difficult in that respect and Goodwood is one of the most difficult. If you are trapped, there's sometimes no way out and jockeys can be made to look foolish through no fault of their own. Mark Of Esteem is exactly the type of horse who could get into trouble. He comes from behind with a great burst of finishing speed. The only problem is getting him in a position to use it.

In the race, from that draw, all I could really do was track the leaders, and it was my old rival Alhaarth, with Willie Carson, and Gothenberg, ridden by Jason Weaver, who shared the lead. Alhaarth was one of the horses who, on 2,000 Guineas day, was said to have been at a disadvantage by racing away from the rails. Many people had complained about the 'uneven watering' as they'd called it, and said that Nick Lees, the clerk of the course, had produced 'unfair ground' for those drawn in the middle. At the time I'd thought it was nonsense, as Alhaarth had been only a couple of horse widths wide of me, and nearly level, as we'd all made our efforts that day. After the Tripleprint race at Goodwood, all those arguments would be dead and buried.

As we came to the crucial stage of the race, I knew I had the first two covered, as I still had plenty of horse and Willie and Jason were already working. But on my outside, Walter Swinburn seemed to be going pretty well on Bishop of Cashel and it soon became obvious that he would not be doing me any favours and letting me out. As I said to the press afterwards, 'Walter had me in prison and I didn't have the key to get out.' Luckily, though, at the furlong and a half point, Gothenberg was starting to weaken and left me a little gap on the inside of Willie and Alhaarth. Remembering what had happened at York just two days before on Russian Snows, I didn't want a repetition, as the consequences could be very difficult. At Goodwood, because of the nature of the track, which is very undulating, horses suddenly left in front on their own, as Alhaarth was about to be, tend to roll on to the far rail. Because I was worried Alhaarth would do that, I had to make my move about twenty yards earlier than I would ideally have done. Jason kind of had to check for a stride, but once Mark Of Esteem went through the gap, he quickened even better than he had in the 2,000 Guineas.

The horse won easily, but as we were pulling up, I saw Jason, who said, 'I had to check when you went for the gap.' I asked him, 'Did I touch you?' and when he replied, 'No, you didn't', that was good enough for me. I thought, 'I'll get away with it.' Obviously, at the back of my mind, there was a little worried voice, because the stewards are getting a bit strict nowadays, and the result wasn't yet official. In fact, it took them fifteen minutes after Jason and I went in to see them. Jason was great, like a good old friend, saying there was no blame on me whatsoever. Then, after the delay, the announcement, 'The placings remain unaltered.' You can imagine how delighted we all were. First Halling and now Mark Of Esteem, two champions showing how good they were in the same week.

Meanwhile, Matt, still looking stunned, and still filming away, and Peter were beginning to look edgy. Because of the inquiry we were between fifteen and twenty minutes late setting off in the taxi for the air strip. Neil was waiting for the short flight to Windsor, and the weather up there was terrible, with heavy rain falling.

I had three rides that night, starting with one for Ian Balding at my minimum 8st 6lb. Because I had been pretty weak the day before and with big rides like Mark Of Esteem and Sharaf Kabeer at Goodwood, I hadn't wanted to weaken myself with a sweat in the morning, but had planned half an hour in the sauna at Windsor. Getting there late meant I had just ten minutes, but I was in there on my own, and got a real good steam going, pouring plenty of water on the fire until it was very hot in there. I gave it a really good bashing, but ran out of time. My natural weight, as I've said before, is at least a stone heavier than the weight at which I manage to ride, and to keep near my riding weight I have to be careful. At the same time, there is nothing I hate more than doing overweight. Over a season of around 1,000 rides, I'm annoyed if I'm ever overweight, and usually three or four times a season, I might be slightly over. I think it's unprofessional, but here I was just a quarter-pound over the limit when I sat on the scales and the form books will record the dreaded words: one pound overweight; 8st 7lb. Ian was very understanding and when the filly I was riding in a handicap race finished well down the field, nobody worried too much that the overweight had made any difference.

When I'd set off in the morning from Newmarket, I'd said to Matt and Peter, looking at my rides, that this was the day of the old-timers. Maybe I should have said 'a reunion of old friends'. Mark Of Esteem, Sharaf Kabeer and Shantou, my ride in a nice conditions race which was coming up next at Windsor, had all done me proud the last time I'd ridden them before my accident. Shantou of course was the horse on which I'd had such a great ride, finishing third in the Derby, but like Mark Of Esteem and also Annus Mirabilis, my final ride of the day half an hour later, he is a bit of a character. I quite enjoy trying to find the key to this type of horse, I find them more interesting. Mark Of Esteem needs to come very late; Shantou is a nice horse, but you have to leave him alone and then ask him for his one run at the two-furlong pole. He was also very disappointing when we thought he would win the King Edward VII Stakes at Royal Ascot and even worse in a less important race at Haydock. I followed my own blueprint for riding him, in what was a pretty good race for a conditions event, and he quickened really well at the two pole and drew clear to win by three and a half lengths from Double Leaf, showing that he liked the easy ground. It was really good to see him back in the winner's circle.

And now to the biggest character of them all and my most difficult ride of the day, the Winter Hill Stakes, a Group 3 race and the most valuable race of the year at Windsor. In fact, Annus Mirabilis, that Saturday night, was probably the most difficult and testing ride for me of the year. He has never run a bad race in his life, but all his tough races against very good opponents may have made him a difficult horse to win with. In the race, I sat behind the leaders and was going well enough to hit the front two furlongs from home. A furlong later, first Storm Trooper and then Salmon Ladder went by me, and nobody could have expected what was going to happen. I still didn't really ask for a final effort until 100 yards from home, and Annus Mirabilis just gradually edged back and got up in the last twenty-five yards, and I don't think I hit him once in that final effort. As far as I was concerned, apart from Mark Of Esteem at Newmarket, when we were in a Classic race and success was so important, this was the best ride of the year. I really kidded him home. It's funny – the day before I'd felt lousy and the thought of having a cameraman follow me around hadn't interested me at all. Matt couldn't have chosen a better day. As we left Windsor, Matt still looked stunned. I'd won a Listed race, a Group 2, a Group 3 and a good conditions race. Overall, in one week, the horses I'd ridden had won more than £400,000 in prize money. My seven per cent of that was not looking too bad. That's what's called timing your comeback, but it's not always like that.

That night, after we flew back to Newmarket, I decided to take Peter and his wife Lucinda out to dinner at the Number Nine restaurant. I didn't watch too closely what Peter ate, but I had Caesar salad and some grilled salmon. As ever, the quality was great. I was really on a high after a great week, and began to look forward to another good Sunday back in Deauville.

The last Sunday of the month-long meeting always features the Grand Prix de Deauville. I was riding for André Fabre, but we finished only fifth behind Paul Cole's good horse Strategic Choice, who was given a lovely ride by Richard Quinn. Then I had another try on Leap For Joy, my ride at Leopardstown soon after the start of my comeback. In the two seasons I've ridden her, Leap For Joy has hardly ever been lucky with getting a run during a race just as she hadn't in Ireland. So I was determined that she would get every chance this time and got her plenty of room to challenge at the two-furlong pole. This time I went too early and she was well beaten by the finish. Already the day wasn't going particularly well and when I rode Chantilly Fashion in the Tiercé race – the horse finished fifth, as usual – it didn't get any better. Chantilly Fashion runs for one of the smaller French stables and they always book me to ride in races like this. If it's Sunday, it's France, and if it's France, it seems, I ride Chantilly Fashion. Tiercé races are always contested by big fields. The French betting public focuses on the Tiercé, where the punter has to get the first three in the correct order. In recent years, the Quarté, first four, and Quinté, first five, have given France's small punters the chance of a big win for small stakes. Racing in England is worried about the effect on betting turnover of competition from the National Lottery. If racing could organise its own regular bet like the Tiercé, Quarté or Quinté, all as in France, all three on the same race, the small punters might come back. At least they can see how their money is going through a race, unlike the lottery, which is just a bag of balls!

The funniest part of my day in Deauville was left for last. The two Bints (Arabic for daughter or girl), Bint Shadayid, ridden by me, and Bint Salsabil, ridden by Willie Carson, formed a strong British challenge for the Prix de la Nonette, a valuable race for fillies run over ten furlongs. Both carry the colours of Sheikh Hamdan, who had the good fortune to own their respective mothers Shadayid, a very good horse, and Salsabil, a great one. They were coupled under the French betting rules, which at present – they are about to change it to the same system as in Britain where all the horses run as individuals – means that a punter backing one coupled horse, wins the bet if the other part of the couple wins the race. So if someone wanted to back Bint Salsabil, and I won instead on Bint Shadayid, the punter would still collect. Two for the price of one! We, jointly, were second favourite behind Luna Wells, a good filly trained by André Fabre and ridden by Thierry Jarnet.

We were both prominent from the start, and as we came to the straight, Willie was lying second and I was third. There had been racing all month at the track, which was beginning to show signs of wear and tear, and by now everyone was beginning to search for better ground away from the inside rail. My rides earlier on convinced me it would be a good idea to get towards the stands side, and, as we turned in, I angled my run towards the stands while Willie stayed up the middle. We had less than two furlongs to go and there were at least four horse widths between us. Then, suddenly, my filly started to see the crowd and began to hang towards Willie. As I was anxious to correct that, I pulled my stick through to my right hand to tell her to go straight. As I did, my whip hit the face of Luna Wells, on whom Thierry Jarnet was trying to come between us. She jerked her head and stopped for a moment. By now the gap is already down to just two horses wide, and then Willie's filly starts to go left looking for company herself. Thierry still persisted going for the gap, but Willie and Bint Salsabil kept hanging towards me so Thierry had no option but to switch round us. At the line, which came up almost immediately, Willie won by a neck, with Luna Wells a length back in third.

As we came back to unsaddle I felt very disappointed to be beaten in a close finish, but the worst was yet to come. Thierry objected to both of us, so we all went into the stewards' room. They showed us the video, and it looked bad. In fact, on the screen, it looked so bad that if you had wanted to do a 'team job' to stop the favourite you couldn't have done it better. Out there, though, it's every man for himself. I was trying to win, Willie Carson was trying to win, and we were out to beat the favourite. We were already out again for the next race when we heard the results of the long stewards' inquiry. We were both demoted – to second and third – and, more painfully, when I came back after the race, I discovered we were banned for four days each. I must say, I can't remember ever being involved before in a race where the first two were disqualified, especially the first two for the same owner in a Group race. I cannot believe that my actions deserved a four-day ban. All I tried to do was correct my filly and unfortunately my whip accidentally caught Luna Wells. Once again, racing, the great equaliser, had thrown a dampener on a great winning spell.

The one saving grace was that the French ban did not get included in my by now worrying 'totting-up' score of eight points. If it had, I would already have been on my way to Portman Square and at least fourteen days' extra holiday. Because of the four days and York, and the French, which fortunately overlapped by one day, I had a total of seven days out of action. I was free to ride, though, in the middle of that on my old friend Germany, back in the same Baden-Baden race he'd won the year before.

I'd already asked John to let me have a couple of days off, so when I returned the following Tuesday to Deauville for the final day of the August meeting I arranged to stay there with Catherine for the rest of the week. I'd gone from doing virtually nothing to going flat-out straight away. The break was a great help before building up to Kempton and the September Stakes with Classic Cliché, then the St Leger meeting and all the important races of the autumn in Europe and around the world.

13 The St Leger

Back in June, when I first had time to think about the implications of my fall, the furthest thing from my mind was being able to ride in the summer at all. In fact, I thought the St Leger meeting was an impossibility, so there would be no chance to wear the famous St Leger hat again.

Of course, my recovery had been so rapid that I had already won plenty of nice races before the 1996 St Leger meeting, and the whole week at Doncaster went very well. I won on a nice two-year-old of John's called Benny The Dip on the Wednesday; won the Doncaster Cup on Thursday on that great stayer Double Trigger because Jason Weaver was suspended; and completed a first and last race double on the Friday.

I did have a little regret on the Friday, though, as I did mess up one race, on Daunt. Immediately after the race I felt it had been a good ride and we'd been beaten fair and square, but, on reflection, if I had allowed him to go on when he was travelling so well at the two-furlong pole, I'm sure we'd have won. Instead, I waited half a furlong – he did have 9st 12lb to carry, after all – and the response when I asked him was a little disappointing.

When I got home that night I had a quick glance at the draw for the following day's Pertemps St Leger. I noticed that I'd drawn stall ten, near the outside, on Shantou, while Dushyantor, the horse I thought our biggest danger, was immediately to my left, in nine, with Gordi and Heron Island, the only two outside us, at eleven and twelve respectively.

Inside myself I was in terrible form. Perhaps I was feeling the race the next day, because at the back of my mind I knew I had a good chance. There was a lot of talk about Shantou being ungenuine. Timeform even gave him a squiggle after his rating, which denotes an ungenuine horse, but to my mind he's just a little bit of a character.

I was very untalkative (you might say unusually so!) that night and went to bed at nine o'clock after Catherine and I had had a light dinner. I had a lot think about. I needed to go through the race in my mind and how best to win it. It was a Classic race after all.

Just as well I had a good night's sleep, because I needed to be up very early the next day. In fact we finished the first lot gallops at John's by six thirty and I came home to study the paper for the day's races. I still wasn't absolutely clear how to approach this race, though, so I decided to go back to John's for breakfast. I had a few questions to put to him and wanted to see if he had the answers. I wanted to race on Dushyantor. He was, after all, the horse to beat, and I reckoned my best chance was to follow him. But John wasn't quite so sure as Shantou is a horse who, if you ask him to do something he doesn't want to do, you would ruin his chance. John said, 'Follow Dushyantor if you can, but take the race as it comes.'

During Doncaster week, I had been booked to do a couple of talks to some guests. On St Leger day, although I didn't have a ride in either of the first two races, I was due to make an appearance for some racegoers, so I left home earlier than I would normally need to do. Lucky I did. The journey took three and a quarter hours, an hour more than usual, and I only just made it in time for the first race. The traffic got even worse later on, and Oscar Urbina, the young Spanish jockey who is doing so well now with my old boss Luca Cumani, arrived only just in time for his first ride in the St Leger, on Mons. When you are preparing yourself for a big race, having to rush and be anxious about whether you are going to be on time is the worst possible thing to happen.

I did have one ride before the big race, in the two-year-old sprint on Head Over Heels. This filly is owned by John's wife Rachel and loves fast ground. The day before, John was hoping the ground would be a little easier for the St Leger than on the other three days, when a couple of track records were set, one by the great Double Trigger. He told the press: 'I hope they leave the taps on all night!' and the reports from the jockeys who rode in the first two races were encouraging for Shantou if not for harmony in the Gosden household. All the family, including John's mother, were there for a family outing, but Head Over Heels was as much in their minds as Shantou.

Head Over Heels finished fourth, as the ground was indeed a little softer than she likes, so now it was all up to Shantou. I came back and reported to John that the ground was very good. Shantou was fine in the build-up and very good at the start. He jumped so well from the stalls that I was actually about a length in front of Dushyantor. I waited four or five strides for Dushyantor to get into a prominent position inside me but he didn't. Shantou was already travelling really well and I managed to get into a prominent position. I noticed Mons and Sharaf Kabeer were in front of me; on my inside was the outsider Samraan – who I thought had no chance – and Gordi was to my right.

Once the race took its rhythm I accepted my position, so even though I had wanted to track Dushyantor, I tried to keep Shantou happy. There wasn't much change until we came to the straight. Obviously, from the position in which I was racing, I was completely boxed in and I was already looking for several horses, especially Dushyantor, to come round and pass me on the outside. Just after the four-furlong pole, so still with a long way to go, I could see Pat and Dushyantor making very good headway and pulling double. I thought: 'We're a long way from home – don't panic!' My main concern at this time was to make sure we got a clear run. Meanwhile, when Pat got to the leaders, he sat on Dushyantor for a bit.

At that stage we were approaching the two-furlong mark and I was hoping to find a way out. Luckily, I found a split and immediately started to feel Shantou move – he came alive. As we made ground towards Pat at the furlong pole, I could see Dushyantor was still going well. Once we passed the furlong, the race was really on. Both horses were going for gold. When we reached half a furlong out, we were going stride for stride, until which time neither Pat nor I had gone for 100 per cent. Till then, we'd asked our horses for ninety-five per cent. Now we both asked for everything, me with my stick in my left hand, Pat with his in his right hand. In the last fifty yards, Dushyantor could not manage to give him any more, but Shantou galloped all the way to the line.

I was lucky to have ridden Mons against Dushyantor in the Great Voltigeur at York a few weeks before. That day

Dushyantor had found extra because he'd been spurred on by the sight of Mons close to him. I was aware of that, so wanted to challenge three or four horses wide of Dushyantor, and keeping the whip in my left hand – the arm I'd broken not so long before – meant Shantou would edge away from Dushyantor towards the stands. It was still only in the last ten yards that we were definitely ahead, and we crossed the line a neck in front. So, once more, the thing I'd been working for, for all those years, came to fruition. I've always thought, 'It can't get better than this', but it always does. As we crossed the line, I screamed and waved at the stands, but really to John. The feeling was pure ecstasy. It was an amazing sensation.

As we came back to the winner's enclosure, I was accompanied by the same two policemen and their police horses who had escorted me on my walk back after Classic Cliché the year before. Bob Herrick, the lad who has done so much to settle Shantou and who rides him out on his own every day, came to collect me. I had worn two pairs of goggles in the race, and gave one to Bob and threw the other into the crowd, which, as at York, gave me the full Yorkshire welcome. While we were still walking in, I couldn't see John as I scanned the crowd. I'd already decided to mark another great occasion with a great jump, and, judging by the picture in the following Monday's *Daily Telegraph*, it was one Angel Cordero would have been proud of!

I landed, gave Sheikh Mohammed, who owns Shantou, a hug and took the saddle off. Then John came in and was grinning from ear to ear. If he didn't have ears, his mouth would have gone all the way round. Then, afterwards, when I'd been in the weighing room for a few seconds, I came out to collect my own trophy, the much-treasured St Leger hat, something every jockey would like to get once. I had two in two years. I was interviewed before the presentation by Brough Scott on Channel 4. I told him what a special moment it was – as good as winning the Derby – for the staff and something I'd wanted so much for John, after all that undeserved criticism.

Then came the presentation. I received the hat. I'll never forget the feeling of standing there on the podium. Then I looked to the left and John was standing off the podium. It was hard to describe the look on his face. A mixture of shock and emotion. It was surprising to see such emotion on the face of such a big, powerful man. I had to walk off the podium and back into the weighing room. If I had stayed, the lump in my throat would have turned to tears. It was all too much for me.

I bought a dozen bottles of champagne for the boys in the weighing room, and at once they all started to come out of the woodwork. There were some big fields for the handicaps that day, and it was soon obvious that the twelve bottles were not going to be enough. I bought another six, and, what with the jockeys, the valets, and a couple of the stall handlers, these soon went too.

Throughout 1996, the good times and the bad times have gone hand-in-hand. I was still on a high and rode two more winners in the last two races for a treble with combined odds of more than 600–1. A few punters struck it rich that day, but, as ever, I was soon coming down to earth. Pat and I both had to see the stewards because, in their opinion, our riding had breached the controversial rule H9 on use of the whip.

I'd been down that path already when I'd won my first Classic of the year, the 2,000 Guineas, when Philip Robinson and Jason Weaver had also paid the penalty for a thrilling finish to a Classic race. Now Pat and I were again in the dock. We watched the video, and I gave Shantou thirteen strokes with the whip, but I explained to the stewards that they were only back-handers and flicks with the whip and not at all severe. The rule, which none of the jockeys thinks is reasonable, meant I could expect a two-day ban for unreasonable frequency – that's what Pat got. But even after I'd explained about the back-handers, they gave me an extra two days for force. I was perplexed by this, because it meant they believed I'd hit the horse harder than anyone else – I had not and seldom do. As Pat said later, unless the stewards of the Jockey Club sort it out, the top jockeys will get banned after every important race.

So once again I paid the price and took it on the chin. Sheikh Mohammed was happy, John was happy, the staff were happy and I'm sure the racing public thought we had put on a great show. It's so ironic.

We drove home and met John later for a quiet drink. I was proud of him, and was so pleased that we had achieved such a great triumph together. He had got his first, much-deserved English Classic winner. I hope to ride for him for many years and, as I told him that night, 'The first one is always the hardest, there's plenty more Classics to come.'

For me this has been an extraordinary year in so many ways. The ups have been great, but there've been far too many downs. Injury, bans and disappointment mixed with some amazing spells of great success. My resolution for 1997 is to have a much more consistent year, free of injury, and, if you're reading this Pat and the rest of you, I'm going all out to get back the title. It was only lent.